Post-Traumatic
Stress Disorder

Post-Traumatic Stress Disorder

A PRACTICAL GUIDE
TO RECOVERY

David Kinchin

Thorsons
An Imprint of HarperCollins*Publishers*

Thorsons
An Imprint of HarperCollins*Publishers*
77–85 Fulham Palace Road,
Hammersmith, London W6 8JB
1160 Battery Street,
San Francisco, California 94111-1213

Published by Thorsons 1994
1   3   5   7   9   10   8   6   4   2

A catalogue record for this book is
available from the British Library

ISBN 0 7225 2955 4

Typeset by Harper Phototypesetters Limited
Northampton, England
Printed in Great Britain by
Mackays of Chatham, Kent

Contents

Introduction

On Saturday 14 July 1990 I was busy at work as a police officer with the traffic department of Thames Valley Police. I had been a police officer for 11 years. My wife and three children were quite happy with my career and I had nearly always managed to leave my work behind me when I went off duty.

The following day, what started off as a routine evening's work ended when I found myself in the centre of a riot. I was surrounded by angry, hostile faces without another police uniform in sight. I was kicked, punched, spat upon and sworn at. I was trapped. For a few terrifying minutes I thought I was going to die.

I had watched other people come to terms with traumatic events, but this was the first time that I had experienced a serious, potentially life-threatening situation myself. I was admitted to hospital with a broken cheekbone and damage to my kidneys and spleen. In the weeks that followed I was also diagnosed as suffering from Post-Traumatic Stress Disorder (PTSD).

I had never heard of Post-Traumatic Stress Disorder and my family doctor acknowledged that I was his first patient to be diagnosed as suffering from the disorder.

I wanted to find out more about PTSD and I wanted to meet other people who had been similarly diagnosed. This was not easy. Almost all texts on the subject had been written by medical experts and academics for peer readership, and trying to find other sufferers to compare notes with was rather like an agoraphobic trying to find another sufferer to talk to. I knew that there must be hundreds around but I didn't know how to contact them.

Eventually I did find other people who were suffering from Post-Traumatic Stress Disorder. A few were fellow police officers, but most were just people who had been unfortunate in finding themselves unexpectedly involved in an extremely traumatic incident **and thought they were going to die.**

As a result of sharing my ideas with many of these people, I decided that I had to write my own book. In the book I would include my own story and the stories of several other PTSD sufferers. The book would be written by a PTSD sufferer, for other PTSD sufferers. This is the book I so badly wanted to read.

◄O►

What is Post-Traumatic Stress Disorder?

09.15 *School's settled down. Teacher is about to mark the register. A call of 'dinner children' from the corridor. Some go to pay their dinner shillings in the hall. Two are spotted by the headmistress, Miss Jennings, and sent to the senior school with a message.*

09.18 *An avalanche crashes through the school. It kills one of the two children on their way to the senior school. A black, wet mass slurps through a classroom, and fills Miss Jennings's study. She's 64, due to retire at the end of term. Next door to her Mrs. Bates and 33 children, aged 10 and 11, all die.*

09.29 *All 11 of the school soccer team, who had won 3-2 the afternoon before, are killed.*

If this were fiction it would be horrifying enough, but the fact that it actually happened gives it a traumatic quality. We live in an age when such events seem to occur with ever-increasing frequency. Not a single day passes without a calamity affecting some part of the planet, and pictures of these events are immediately flashed to our TV screens and our newspapers. The disadvantage of having such an efficient and prompt news service is that everyone becomes better acquainted with the dangers life may have in store. We are all more traumatically cognizant.

Apart from headline-making disasters, there are other sources of trauma. All around, people become victims of crime and accidents, quite often with devastating consequences. Many of these events go unnoticed except for the few people who have been directly affected by such ordeals, but many of the victims may later suffer from Post-Traumatic Stress Disorder (PTSD).

Trauma is defined in the *Oxford English Dictionary* as 'a powerful shock that may have long-lasting consequences'. The effects of trauma can be immediately overwhelming.

PTSD results when a person has been exposed to an event which is outside the range of normal human experience: an event which would markedly distress almost anyone. It is the very normal human response to a very abnormal situation. The experience could be a serious threat to life. It could be a serious threat or actual harm to one's children, partner or other close relative or friend. It could be the sudden destruction of one's home or community; or seeing another person who has recently been seriously injured or killed as the result of either an accident or physical violence.

PTSD goes further. The event only has to be perceived as traumatic by the victim. In reality the incident might not pose a serious threat to life, but if the incident is genuinely considered to be life-threatening, then the victim has experienced an event outside the range of normal human experience.

I believe that PTSD is very much the product of modern living. PTSD case numbers rise in ratio to advances in technology. The more advanced today's world becomes, the greater the scope for the existence of severe life stresses and traumatic situations. The more advanced

2

our communications networks become, the more our minds are filled with plausible traumatic imagery. I suspect the incidence of PTSD cases will continue to rise.

Large scale disasters, either natural or man-made, will inevitably lead to a large number of people within one community being affected by PTSD. On 21 October 1966, a waste tip from a Welsh coalfield slid down the side of a valley and demolished several houses and a village school. The incident at Aberfan, near Merthyr Tydfil, killed 116 children and 28 adults.[1] The opening paragraph describes part of this disaster. In less than 20 minutes every person in that community had been permanently scarred by a disaster which touched the hearts of millions.

This disaster is vividly recalled by many Britons because it was covered by television crews who arrived on the scene within hours. The full horror and traumatic consequences of the disaster were screened in millions of homes.

Five-and-a-half years later, a similar event happened in the USA. On 26 February 1972 an enormous slag dam gave way and unleashed thousands of tonnes of water on the communities of Buffalo Creek, West Virginia. The mining hamlets of Becco, Lundale and Pardee were almost totally destroyed.[2] The disaster resulted in 126 deaths, and it left 4,000 people homeless. Like the Aberfan tragedy, the actual incident lasted less than 20 minutes, but the consequences were devastating.

In 1966, the people of Aberfan were considered to be suffering from 'severe shock'. In 1972, those in Buffalo Creek were labelled as suffering from a complex which became journalistically known as 'Buffalo Creek syndrome'.

After seeing so many traumatized Vietnam veterans, the

medical profession recognized that all victims of extremely traumatic events tended to exhibit very similar behaviour and symptoms. Significant numbers of Vietnam veterans were displaying signs that all was not well with their lives. Their traumatic wartime experiences were adversely affecting their state of health. Upon returning home they were not welcomed as heroes. Civilians just did not want to know. The combination of suffering severe trauma and experiencing such a negative reaction back home led some veterans to resort to drink, drugs and violence.

In 1980, the symptoms exhibited by these veterans, and those exhibited by civilian victims such as those who suffered at Buffalo Creek, were grouped together under the diagnosis of Post-Traumatic Stress Disorder. The definition, coded DSM-III, gave a name to the disorder and officially replaced such terms as: shell shock (1940); gross stress reaction (1952); transient situation disturbance (1968); and Buffalo Creek Syndrome (1972).

In 1987, this definition was revised (DSM-III-R) and is now recognized world wide.

In the wake of the terrorist act which caused the Lockerbie plane crash, many of the rescue workers struggled to cope with the horrific scenes before their eyes. By the date of this disaster, 21 December 1988, it was readily acknowledged that these people were suffering from Post-Traumatic Stress Disorder.

Set out in table form, the criteria appear very cold and clinical. Examples used later will add a considerable degree of reality to the disorder and make these symptoms more understandable.

Five criteria need to be met before a diagnosis of Post-Traumatic Stress Disorder can be made.

---

1 The person must have witnessed or experienced a serious threat (real or perceived) to his or her life or physical well-being.
2 The person must re-experience the event, or part of the event, in some form.
3 The person must persistently avoid situations associated with the trauma, or experience a numbing of general responsiveness.
4 The person must experience persistent symptoms of increased arousal, or 'over-awareness'.
5 Symptoms must have lasted at least a month.

HOW MANY PEOPLE SUFFER FROM PTSD?

The number of people who suffer from PTSD at any one time is equal to about one per cent of the general population. In 1987, researchers carried out a survey of psychological disorders exhibited by the population of St Louis, Missouri.[3] A total of 2,500 randomly selected residents were studied, and 28 were diagnosed as suffering from PTSD.

Of those 28, the men cited only two types of event as a cause of the disorder: combat and witnessing someone hurt or die. The most common event cited by the women was physical attack, including rape. Other events which were identified as triggering the PTSD were being poisoned, and having a miscarriage. Major disasters accounted for none of the 28 cases.

Within some groups of society, the incidence of PTSD

must be expected to be much higher than one per cent. Within the emergency services (fire, police and ambulance) and the armed forces (army, navy and air force) the incidence of PTSD can be as high as 15 per cent.[4] It is a disturbing probability that out of every hundred police officers currently engaged in uniformed patrol duties in our towns and cities, 15 will be suffering from symptoms in accord with PTSD.

Post-Traumatic Stress Disorder
High risk groups

High risk groups	Risk
Shipwreck survivors	75%
Bombing survivors	50%
Hijack survivors	37%
Rape victims	33-50%
Abuse victims	50%
Combat victims	25-50%
Air crash survivors	22%
Emergency service staff	15%
GENERAL POPULATION	1%

In some instances, the individual may have experienced a prolonged series of stressful circumstances. A Vietnam veteran may have experienced several traumatic combat incidents over a period of weeks or months. A fire officer may deal with a run of house fires in which children have been fatally burned. In cases like these, the extensive stress can result in Prolonged Duress Stress Disorder (PDSD) which results in the same symptoms as PTSD.

If you are a PTSD sufferer, you may feel alone, but you are not.

IS WHAT I AM EXPERIENCING NORMAL?

There are over 6,000 million people on this planet. Consequently, there are the same number of different reactions to any situation. No two people will have an identical reaction to one event. That is what makes us human. Two people who experience the same event together will react to it differently. If there are two hundred people present, the variety of reactions is multiplied by that number. The only difference in a large group is that several people may have broadly similar reactions. Confronted by a traumatic situation some will face it, others will move away. This reaction is referred to as 'fight or flight'. If the event is particularly traumatic, many will run the risk of developing PTSD.

Who can say what is normal? What can be said, without fear of contradiction, is that a person who is faced with an abnormal situation will react *in some way* to that situation. How the person reacts will depend on many other factors, such as previous experiences, mood at the time of the event, and individual perception of the threat to personal safety.

Suppose you are leaving the theatre one evening and you come face to face with a youth. He waves a sharp knife under your nose and demands all your cash. It is likely that you first feel fear, then anger, then logic takes over and you reason that no amount of cash is worth a slashed face. The youth grins wildly, waves your money under your gaze to signify his victory, and runs off.

If, three weeks later, you are leaving a cinema and someone rushes up to you brandishing your forgotten coat, your first reaction is one of panic. Your mind, briefly, links the two events because some aspects of the first traumatic event have been repeated in the second, friendly, incident. Most people familiar with the circumstances of the robbery will see your initial panic reaction as normal. People witnessing the second event, not knowing about the robbery, might consider your initial panic as rather unusual. It is all a matter of perception and understanding.

Radiation is widely perceived as a threat to life. Few of us fully understand it or can visualize it, but we all know it can kill. In March 1979 there was a radiation 'incident' at Three Mile Island in America.

Three Mile Island is situated near Harrisburg, Pennsylvania. The incident which took place was contained within the power station complex. There was no real risk to the residents of the town. However, only a few months before that incident, a film describing a fictional nuclear accident had been released. *The China Syndrome,* starring Jane Fonda, told the story of a negligent power company searching for greater profits at the expense of safety. The result was the ultimate nightmare of a nuclear meltdown.

The nuclear lobby rubbished *The China Syndrome* as totally alarmist. However, at Three Mile Island, Hollywood drama was being acted out in real life. Naturally, people's perceptions of the risks involved had been altered by the film. There were no fatalities in Pennsylvania, but large numbers of people panicked and became severely traumatized by the incident. In the circumstances, this panic was both normal and reasonable.

Sadly, the situation was to be repeated in 1986, this time at Chernobyl in Russia. The consequences on that occasion were far more devastating.

AM I GOING MAD?

Post-Traumatic Stress Disorder is not a mental illness. It is an emotional condition, from which it is possible to make a full recovery.[5]

The most distressing symptom of PTSD is the re-living of the traumatic event, whether you want to or not. This re-experiencing may take the form of recurrent nightmares, or daytime flashbacks. In either case you are troubled by vivid, repetitive pictures of the trauma. Sometimes these pictures are so real that you start to behave as though the event is happening all over again. This re-experiencing may last only a few seconds, but on the other hand it might last hours or even days initially. Often you are fully aware of what is happening but can do nothing to control the situation. The flashbacks can occur with distressing frequency, adding fuel to the erroneous belief that you are 'going mad'.

The memory of the event is usually in picture form. Sounds and smells can act as a trigger to start off the picture sequence. Former Middle East hostage, Terry Waite, tells how the sound of ripping masking tape triggered off terrible memories of his days in captivity.[6] Chained and blindfolded in a tiny cell, he was frequently moved from one 'safe house' to another. Before every move he was bound with masking tape; even his mouth and eyes were covered. It is little wonder that such a harmless and familiar sound to many should be such a traumatic trigger for him.

Because these vivid flashbacks are so unpredictable, victims find themselves at a disadvantage. Former friends and colleagues may feel insecure and unsure about how to react. Canteen chatterers may start to label the victim as a 'nutter' or a 'head case'. These labels are not appropriate to anyone, and they are certainly not appropriate descriptions of a PTSD victim. Sadly, the labels tend to stick. Victims start to panic. They avoid situations or activities which are likely to trigger the images. Their lifestyle changes and they start to lose contact with other people.

This spiral of events may lead to feelings of depression and anxiety. Untreated, this can have dangerous and far-reaching consequences. Resultant poor attendance at the work place may result in unemployment, and irritability often adds strain to all personal relationships. All this, combined with possible uncontrollable and violent outbursts during periods when the victim is re-experiencing the trauma, can add up to a totally unbearable life. Things cannot continue in this way for long.

In seeking medical help, the last straw for PTSD victims is to picture themselves as mentally irredeemable cases doomed to spend the rest of their lives in a Dickensian style institution for the insane.

This is a totally false expectation, but one common to many PTSD sufferers. They are not mad, but they do require specialized help.

WHY ME?

If every person who ever experienced a traumatic event *always* suffered from PTSD, the disorder would become almost as common as colds or flu. Clearly not everyone is affected to the same degree. Why?

Research studies that have examined the causes of PTSD are scarce. It is still very difficult to identify those most likely to be affected, and those at greatest risk. Very little of the research is conclusive and any figures quoting a person's 'PTSD risk' are likely to be contested by various bodies having a vested interest in either under-estimating or over-estimating the figures. Defence departments will play down the figures. When asked about PTSD cases, the Ministry of Defence in London claimed that only 68 individual British combat troops received any form of psychiatric treatment as a direct result of the Gulf War. The independent group, 'Gulf Families Crisis Line', claims that the figure is at least 13,000. The truth is probably somewhere in between.

First, it is necessary to look at the groups of people likely to suffer with PTSD.

GROUP		% chance of developing PTSD
Primary victims	(survivors)	45%
Secondary victims	(family and friends)	80%
Tertiary victims	(onlookers and witnesses)	40%
The rescuers	(the emergency services)	15%
The carers	(medical staff and counsellors)	15%

PRIMARY VICTIMS

Primary victims are those who actually experienced the life-threatening situation first hand. In many instances they are easily identified. The survivors of a major disaster stand a 30-60 per cent risk of developing Post-Traumatic Stress Disorder. The risk will vary according to the degree of perceived risk, the duration, and the scale of the event. In many of these cases, people now anticipate a reaction to the trauma. Allowances are made for the victims and it is generally acknowledged that they have experienced an incredible shock. Those involved in a well-publicized tragedy will be overwhelmed by the warmth and compassion of the sympathy expressed towards them.

The novelty wears off after a while. As time passes, those around the victim may be heard to comment that 'It's time she snapped out of it', or 'He should pull himself together and get on with life'. Comments like these show a lack of understanding of PTSD.

Not all primary victims are so obvious. Many life-threatening events go totally unnoticed by the rest of society. A rape victim may hide her trauma for months, or even years. A victim of incest may always feel unable to disclose the abuse. An abused child may simply be labelled hyperactive, or uncontrollable. Many of the children taken into care for their own protection and welfare are actually suffering from some of the symptoms of PTSD.[7] These very personal traumatic experiences are the most difficult to talk about, and the most difficult to treat.

SECONDARY VICTIMS

The family and friends of victims often become victims of PTSD themselves. There are two main reasons for this. First, the family may actually witness scenes from the trauma, either first hand, or by courtesy of the media. For example, many people lost loved ones in the Lockerbie air crash in 1988, where 259 people died. They cannot have avoided seeing the scene on television screens during the following weeks. Seeing the devastation to the community of Lockerbie and the contorted frame of the nose of the aircraft in an open field, could only add to the image of the suffering that might have been endured by a relative or friend.

Those close to the survivors of a disaster may also suffer in a similar way. In recent years Europe has witnessed two traumatic incidents which involved crowded football stadiums. In May 1985, 56 people died during crowd disturbances at the Heysel Stadium in Belgium. Four years later, overcrowding at the Hillsborough Stadium in England resulted in the deaths of 95 people. The last of these victims lived until 1993 when mechanical life support was suspended. Both incidents involved supporters of Liverpool Football Club, and both events were screened live on television. Relatives and friends watched the live television pictures in horror as people were crushed before their eyes, knowing that somewhere in the crowd was a person they cared deeply for.

Once the survivors returned to the relative safety of their homes, they began to suffer vivid memories of the life-threatening event. Those around them also had mental images of the occasion, and witnessing the primary victim's suffering induced the disorder in secondary victims.

This sequence of events is not limited to disasters that have been broadcast on television. Many relatives witness the trauma first hand if it is a road accident, an assault, or a crime against property such as theft or burglary.

TERTIARY VICTIMS

Tertiary victims are the onlookers or witnesses. They have no link with any person directly involved in the life-threatening event, but they saw what happened. If the event is serious, these victims will probably be called to court or a hearing of some kind to give evidence. Giving evidence is a trauma in itself. The worry of such an ordeal hanging over them for months, sometimes years, means that witnesses are not permitted the luxury of forgetting. Society demands that they keep the memory fresh.

Witnesses, like primary victims, just happen to be there at the time. However, if you are so close to an event that you see it, then before long you are nagged by the thought that 'it could have happened to me'. If it is a road accident then that is not an irrational thought, it is a reality. In consequence, the witnesses may also feel that they have been prey to a life-threatening event. They could have been seriously injured or killed.

THE RESCUERS AND THE CARERS

To a degree, the only victims of PTSD who can prepare themselves to deal with life-threatening events are rescuers and carers. Their very job demands that they become involved with primary victims. This involvement is on a very deep and personal level for fire, police and ambulance personnel, doctors, nurses, paramedics and counsellors.

Many of these professional people wear a uniform. This may assist at the time. Hiding behind a uniform can be an asset in certain circumstances. But when the uniform is removed, all that remains is another frail human being. True, this is a well-trained, experienced and professional person, but he or she may only face a major disaster once or twice in their career.

In less traumatic situations, it may be one aspect of the incident which affects professionals in a way that could not have been predicted. In the Lockerbie incident, emergency staff suffered from shock brought about by the meaninglessness of the tragedy. Cases of PTSD were being diagnosed up to two years after the disaster.

The victims of PTSD are many. Those who are not primary victims of the disorder are frequently referred to as hidden victims. For every primary victim of PTSD there could be as many as three hidden victims.

SO WHY ME?

PTSD is selective. Not everyone is affected. Unfortunately, it is not possible to predict who will be affected by the disorder.

There are some indications, however, that particular groups of people *may* be more susceptible to the disorder than others. People who possess an introverted personality may be at slightly greater risk. A family history of anxiety or depression may be a contributing factor. These ideas are based upon very limited research studies purely because *PTSD is such a difficult disorder to monitor.*

It appears likely that a person with pre-existing difficulties that create a stressful lifestyle, may have already stretched his or her psychological and emotional defences to near breaking point. The life-threatening trauma will be the final straw.

Carers and rescue workers can have risks reduced by careful training and preparation to expect trauma. Once a traumatic event has been experienced, the personnel involved must be fully, and professionally, counselled in a procedure known as Critical Incident Debriefing. [8]

Nevertheless, a trauma may be so devastating that it affects even the strongest character. It is unreasonable for anyone to suggest that PTSD is self-induced or that *if only you could pull yourself together things would be just fine.*

In this opening chapter we have looked at trauma, and what Post-Traumatic Stress Disorder is. We have also looked at the number of people who suffer with the disorder, and who they might be. Finally, we have established that victims with PTSD are most definitely 'normal' and are not mad. PTSD is a normal emotional reaction to an abnormal, and potentially life-threatening event.

Before looking at the symptoms and treatments of PTSD, I want to introduce you to a group of people. They are all PTSD victims. They are all real people with feelings and emotions, with families and friends. These are true stories but, quite naturally, the identities have been camouflaged to protect their privacy and confidentiality.

Ten cases are outlined in some detail in the next chapter. These cases reappear throughout the book in an attempt to explain how these people have combatted their PTSD.

The first story is my own.

Chapter two

Personal stories

CASE 1: DAVID

I was 35 years old when all this happened. I live, together with my wife and three children, in a quiet Oxfordshire village. I had been a police officer for 12 years. Before that I taught geography in a secondary school. The incident occurred on 15 July 1990.

We arrived in Wantage Market Place at 8.45 p.m. and Tom stopped the car. From this vantage point there was a perfect view of the town centre. Tonight it was not the view we expected. The place was packed with people.

Whatever the event had been, it was now over. A street cleaning vehicle was clearing rubbish. Judging by the large number of plastic mugs scattered around, a good time had been had by all. The general mood of the crowd was friendly.

A middle-aged male cautiously approached our car. He obviously had a problem.

'I know you two are traffic officers, so you may not be interested ... but there is a fight going on around the other side of the square.'

We spotted the fight. Surrounding the two fighters were about 20 youngsters, jeering and egging them on.

We moved in to separate the pair. If we could break up the fight and calm things down, the crowd would soon disperse.

I caught hold of 'Curly', grabbing his arm and steering him away from his opponent. Tom went to the other youth. I did not see Tom again for some considerable time.

The jeering crowd, acting as if directed, split in two: half moving away with Tom, the other half staying with me. I led 'Curly' to the side of our car, still expecting that after a few words he would calm down and listen to reason.

Wrong.

His friends tried to pull him away, saying I was picking on him. 'Curly' lashed out, hitting my cheek.

This blow made me revise my assessment of the situation. This was not a problem that could be solved quickly and quietly. The crowd was growing all the time. The pulling and shoving continued but I held on to 'Curly's' arm. I was struck again. The situation was becoming ugly. A tactical withdrawal was required, but I did not want to surrender completely.

'I am arresting you...' I started, surprised at my calm voice.

Before I could finish, 'Curly' held up his clenched fists, boxing style, and jeered at me: 'Go on then.'

This seemed to be a golden opportunity. While his fists were raised, I brought my handcuffs out and locked one cuff on to his wrist, in one swift movement. My confidence was restored by this successful manoeuvre. Getting the other cuff on was not so easy.

My senses were on red alert by this time. I was surrounded on three sides. My back was to the car. The group pushed forward and I became pinned to the car. Several kicks made contact with the lower half of my body. I tried to push back, and at the same time move 'Curly' to a position between me and the crowd. If they were going to continue kicking, then he could shield me.

There was a rip. Part of my shirt vanished into the crowd. A loud cheer followed.

All I wanted was to get my prisoner into the car, and get out of the square. I twisted the empty half of the handcuffs so that if 'Curly' wanted to keep his arm he would have to follow it. I eventually manoeuvred him between me and the crowd. I was still pinned to the car, so opening its door was impossible.

Then I was knocked to my knees. A kick caught the side of my leg and I went down. When you are on your knees in a crowd you get a different perspective of things. The situation was decidedly unhealthy.

I knew that if I were knocked any lower I would be in very serious trouble. As well as being on my knees I had my head pinned against the side of the car. While I was still in this vulnerable position I felt several blows to my body. I was in considerable pain, and felt very frightened.

My left hand was gripping the handcuff. My truncheon was in its long slim pocket running down my right leg. It seemed to take forever to find the strap and work it into a position where I could slide my whole hand through the loop and have a firm grip on the weapon.

I had never used my truncheon before. Out it came, almost unnoticed in the chaos. I had a really firm grip on it, and hit out as hard as I could. Being in a sea of legs, I could not miss. I hit out repeatedly. My attackers retreated enough for me to stand up. I could not see anyone hobbling, but the force of those blows had achieved the desired effect. I was back on my feet and had space to manoeuvre at last. I was still scared.

The radio. All this time I had a personal radio on a strap around my waist. I pulled it up to my mouth and pressed the transmit button.

'Tango Whiskey One Four, urgent assistance required, Wantage Market Place.' I repeated the message. I heard no response, and did not know whether the control room had heard me. Perhaps I simply could not hear the reply because of the noise.

To use the radio I had to let go of the handcuff. I also lost my truncheon. I was hit many times and my memory of exactly what happened next is lost forever.

I saw a police uniform before me. It was not Tom, so my message must have got through. I looked around. I could count only three other blue uniforms. The odds were still not favourable.

I saw someone inside the patrol car about to smash the radio. I reached in and caught the handset just in time. I pressed the 'transmit' button. The red transmission light came on. Using this set, my message would go straight to force headquarters.

'Tango Whiskey One Four, 10-9 Wantage Market Place.' It was all I had time for. The message was coded, 10-9 meant an officer required immediate assistance.

I could see Tom, and four others with their truncheons drawn, in a semi-circle, facing outwards. Clearly we still had a fight on our hands. By now there were about 60 youths involved, with many more jeering and shouting.

A police van arrived. After the doors were opened there were a few seconds delay before a large German Shepherd dog emerged. It was barking and straining on its lead.

The handler let the dog advance. Clearly the animal was eager, but it was also confused. It was facing a group in which it was police officers who were holding weapons – their truncheons. The police dog launched its attack, biting the only police sergeant present at the incident. The handler pulled the dog back and scolded it. The dog sat down, totally confused and no longer inclined to take any further part. The crowd sensed the creature's indecision and charged it. The animal was now as frightened as the rest of us. I had never seen a police dog intimidated in this way before, and realized our position was serious. Were we going to be lynched?

I still had hold of the handcuffs, but was starting to tire. I could not keep going much longer. 'Curly' kneed me in the groin, and someone else banged my head several times on my car. I was having difficulty concentrating. I could feel things slipping away.

I looked up. There, 100 feet above me was a police helicopter.

I had not heard it at all. To this day I have no recollection of the noise one associates with a helicopter. It was training a search-light on the group in which I was trapped. I was reassured by its presence, but it spotlighted me as a vulnerable target. It also attracted more people out from the pubs.

At last, some blue flashing lights. There is something very reassuring about the sight and sound of fast, powerful, police patrol cars. Three arrived at the same time, together with the first of four large riot vans each containing 10 officers. The helicopter had at least conveyed the message that we needed help in a big way.

Soon I handed over my prisoner to another officer. The relief at being able to relax my arms was amazing. I looked about me and took stock of the situation. I was aware of chanting:

'Get the Pigs'

'Kill the Bill'

The crowd had grown to over 200, with about 60 involved in the fighting. There were now 50 policemen present, and more still arriving.

Someone suggested that Tom and I take our car, with two prisoners, to the police station. I pushed two prisoners into the car; one of them was 'Curly'. Tom got into the driving seat. As I tried to climb into the back of the car with the two prisoners, the crowd surged forward. I was pinned between door and frame.

A woman approached; I supposed that she was related to one of the prisoners. I thought she intended to tell her son precisely what she thought of his behaviour. She came towards me, looked me straight in the eyes, and spat in my face.

As the crowd was forced back by other officers, I managed to get into the car, stunned by the woman's actions. The ordeal was not over. The crowd forced forward again and rocked the car.

I briefly recalled a television news clip about an incident in Northern Ireland where a mob attacked a car which contained two soldiers. I remembered how the incident concluded, with both men being murdered, and quickly pushed the thoughts out of my mind.

The sideways movement of the car was sickening.

One of the prisoners started to cry. Tom drove the car forward, very slowly. As a gap opened in the crowd he accelerated away to the police station.

CASE 2: MARLENE

Marlene is divorced. She is 43 and lives in Washington State. She served for a time in the armed services but has now settled into a nursing career in a hospital. The incidents she describes occurred in December 1990 and January 1993.

It had been raining for hours. Many of the roads were flooded with surface water that made driving tricky, sometimes dangerous. I hated driving in this sort of weather although I had never even seen a road accident, let alone been involved in one.

I came towards a junction where the surface water was particularly deep. Cars were crossing on to my side of the road in order to go around the water. I slowed right down and came to a gentle halt.

A large truck was coming towards me. The driver clearly did not appreciate how deep the water was and so made no attempt to skirt around the hazard. He drove his vehicle straight through the water, making a bow-wave immediately in front of his own vehicle. As it drew nearer I realized that my little car was in danger of being swamped. I sounded my horn and flashed the car headlamps to try to draw attention to my plight.

The truck trundled past, sending a torrent of water cascading over my vehicle. The engine coughed and sputtered in protest at the sudden deluge of water, then it cut out altogether. It refused to restart.

Furious, I opened my door and clambered out into the road, and the pouring rain. A horn sounded behind me. I turned to see a car. Moments later it struck me, lifting me high on to the front of the vehicle and carrying me about 20 yards along the road before coming to a stop.

I slid on to the road surface and passed out.

My next memory is of a very wet road, only inches from my eyes. I was in pain everywhere and was soaked to the skin. Looking around as much as I could, I saw several people coming to my assistance – and the car that had hit me was driving off. I passed out again.

Two years later, I was a passenger in a friend's car. We were out on a shopping spree, and looking forward to spending our money. We came to a stop at a road junction and my friend was just about to pull out on to the main road when there was a sickening jolt.

My next recollection is one of a stabbing pain in my neck. My car seat appeared to have vanished. The back of it had collapsed and I was resting at a crazy angle, unable to move. Right beside my window was the front of another car. We had been hit from behind and the impact had caused the other car to spin around so that it was wedged against my door. I could not get out, and the car engine was smoking steadily.

I remember thinking, 'Why me again?' and starting to cry.

Someone was touching my left shoulder gently. I looked around to see a friendly face encouraging me to move across to the other side of the car so as to clamber out. I tried to move but could not get myself off the broken seat.

The face grinned, and produced a large, sharp penknife. He moved forward, bringing the knife up towards my neck. I screamed. Then I almost fell off the seat on to my rescuer. He had cut the seat belt which was preventing me from climbing out of the car. Feeling a total fool, I managed to follow him across the seats and on to the road. My legs were like jelly, and I hurt everywhere.

Sitting on the grass at the side of the road, someone offered me a blanket which I gratefully accepted. I was now shaking badly. I looked across at the two cars which, inexplicably, were in the middle of the road. My friend's car was a mess. The other car was in flames. I watched in horror as the flames spread like some kind of infection from one vehicle to the other. In no time at all, the spot where I had been sitting became a ball of dancing red and yellow flames.

The shaking grew steadily worse.

CASE 3: JESSICA

Jessica was 30 at the time of this event. She is married and has one daughter. She works part-time in a local grocery store in southern Pennsylvania where she now lives. Jessica suffered for many years before her condition was recognized as PTSD. The incident took place in January 1981.

I was nine months pregnant and feeling on top of the world until that morning when I realized the time had come for me to give birth. I had enjoyed the pregnancy, survived the morning sickness and revelled in the attention I received from my family and friends. It had previously been agreed that the best way for the baby to be born was by Caesarean section, so off to the hospital I went.

I was well prepared. My bag had been packed for several weeks, new nightdresses and toiletries had been purchased well in advance. I was booked into the hospital ward and introduced to some of the nursing staff. They were all very warm and welcoming. It was my first baby but I assured myself that these people had done it all many times before and that I was in very safe hands.

It came to the time when I was taken from the ward, along endless corridors to the operating suite. I felt rather vulnerable stretched out on the trolley bed. All I was able to do was watch the ceiling as I was moved from one area to another. I noticed cracks and peeling paint, all manner of uninteresting things. The longer the journey lasted the more anxious I became. Eventually, I arrived at the entrance to the operating suite.

I was left alone. Looking about me, I saw that I had a clear view into the operating theatre. The door was wide open. I was being watched constantly by the anaesthetist. I could see all the staff in masks, green clothes and green boots on their feet. I was terrified. The room in which they stood looked sterile and cold. It was full of equipment, shiny surfaces and bright lights.

I was on a trolley, or gurney, but suddenly someone put the sides up like metal bars on the side of a cot. There was no warning of what was happening. Nobody spoke to me. I suddenly felt very lonely. Oh, I felt so closed in by the bars and there appeared to be no escaping my fate.

I was left like this for nearly 30 minutes because the

obstetrician who was going to perform the operation had not yet arrived. During that time, I could see them all walking in and out and looking down at me. In that situation, 30 minutes can seem like an age. I started to think seriously about all the things that could go wrong. I desperately wanted a reassuring voice to talk to. Someone to hold my hand perhaps, and tell me it would all be all right. By the end of the 30 minutes I was convinced that I was going to die in that operating theatre. All around me there were voices talking in hushed, giggling tones about me. I wanted to jump off the trolley and run, run anywhere. It seems impossible, but I had forgotten about the baby, my husband, everything. All I could think of was escaping the operating theatre and almost certain death. That's the last thing I remember.

When I came round after the operation I was a different person. My baby was safe and well, but I was a nervous wreck. I was jumpy. The slightest noise startled me. I found myself constantly studying the rest of the ward, on the watch for any possible dangers. It was crazy. What possible danger could I be in, in a hospital ward?

I dreaded the doctors or nurses pulling the curtains around my bed. It felt so claustrophobic. I started having nightmares about doctors with knives in their hands walking towards me. It was terrifying, and in the time I stayed in hospital I developed a fear of moving outside the ward. I just could not, and did not want to go out.

When I was home it got worse. I ignored the door-bell. I used to run past the telephone in the house. I was actually frightened of the object. When it rang I was petrified. I never answered it, my feet and legs turned to jelly, I felt sick in my stomach. I had panic attacks. I just couldn't understand what had happened to me.

CASE 4: GRAHAM

Graham is 48. He lives with his wife in a detached house in rural Cumbria. He was due to retire from the fire service in seven years time and had already started making plans to emigrate to Australia to join his son's young family. He had worked on the department as a Senior Fire Officer for the past 15 years and was also a very experienced driver. The incident occurred in October 1988.

My story is very short and simple. It was late one night and I was out in my Fire Officer's car, a white Ford with the word 'FIRE' in big bold letters along the side. I was driving. My young colleague and I were listening to the police radio band. A police vehicle was chasing a stolen motorcycle.

By following the commentary we realized that the stolen vehicle was heading our way. We started to head towards a spot where we might intercept the chase. If there was an accident we may be called upon to cut people free of the wreckage. It was a task we had done before. By anticipating such an incident we could save precious moments if an accident occurred.

We were on the edge of the suburbs, on a fast route which bypassed the city centre. Many minor roads passed over the route on specially constructed over-bridges. As was often the case, groups of young people were gathering on some of these bridges to watch the traffic go by. With little other local entertainment, this was quite a normal occurrence, but one which was generally discouraged by the local police.

The stolen motorcycle was only about two miles away and we were rapidly closing the gap between us. The fire car was fitted with blue flashing lights which were now switched on to warn other motorists as we sped along the road in the outside lane at about 80 mph. There was very little traffic on this section of road, and we were making good progress. Our car was capable of 120 mph, and I gently started to increase its speed.

I had been involved in incidents like this hundreds of times before. Even so, I still felt very alert and keen to be of assistance if required.

We were about 500 yards from one of the overbridges, and I was aware of a small group of youngsters standing on the bridge above our lane of traffic. The street lights were not particularly good, but I could see a few of the youngsters jumping up and down, waving their arms about. I suspected they had been drinking. The chill in the air would soon drive them all home, I hoped.

Then I saw the brick. One youth was holding it high above his head. He was going to throw it at our car. I thought the chance of timing his throw exactly right was only slim, but I didn't particularly want a brick to smash through our windscreen whilst we were travelling at ... almost 90 mph now. My concentration became divided between driving and watching the youth with the brick.

Everything shifted into a kind of slow motion. The distance between our car and the bridge decreased steadily. The youth's arms windmilled forward and I saw the brick launch into the air. I was unable to take my eyes off it. My right foot moved from the accelerator pedal to the brake pedal, but it took an age to leave one and find the other. I pushed down on the brake, but the car seemed very slow to respond to the pressure.

My colleague shouted a warning, but that too was in slow motion. My arms moved the steering wheel to the left so as to move from the path of the brick as it dropped towards us. It only measured nine inches by four inches, but it looked so big now.

Suddenly the windscreen shattered and I felt a stabbing pain in my head and shoulder. The car hit one of the bridge supports and came to a halt on the grass beside the road and I sank back into the driving seat. There was a big hole in the windscreen, just to my side of the centre. I could see my colleague using the radio but was unable to hear what he was saying. I don't even remember hearing the windscreen smash.

There was a lot of blood around. We were both bleeding from cuts on our faces and I could not move my left shoulder. We appeared to sit on our own, in silence, for an age before friendly faces started to appear. First to arrive was a police car, then an ambulance. I remember thinking that someone was going to have to cut me free from all this, then I mentally switched off and cannot remember much more.

CASE 5: CINDY

Cindy is 19 years old. She is single and lives with her parents in a semi-detached house on the edge of a town in Norfolk. Having dropped out of school, she is now trying to make up for her lack of qualifications by training as a computer programmer. Prior to the incident in June 1990, Cindy had an extrovert nature.

I was heavily into punk rock. I had the crazy Mohican hairstyle, coloured blue and red. I wore studs in both ears and in my nose. My clothes identified me as an individual with very bad taste. I liked loud music and even louder friends.

Each day, after college, I would walk along the High Street towards the bus station where I had to wait at least 30 minutes for my bus to take me out of town to where I lived with my parents. I often walked along the street with my personal stereo blasting my ears into my kind of heaven. I was totally oblivious to the rest of the world. I didn't care what people thought, did or said. I was my own master.

On the day of the accident, I left college a little late. Even so, I knew I had plenty of time to walk to the bus station. The stereo was on full power. The other people around me could probably hear the music too.

One of the main stores in the High Street was being renovated. Scaffolding had been erected around the structure and numerous posters apologized for any inconvenience that these alterations may cause. The promised completion date had already passed and there was no sign that the work was nearly finished except for the increased number of goods vehicles making deliveries that day.

I had lost interest in the building work long ago. I simply saw it as another obstacle which hindered my progress towards the bus station. The footpath was considerably narrowed by the building work and, in consequence, people were forced to walk that much more closely together than they would normally. It felt as if my own personal space was being invaded by strangers. I didn't like it, but no way was I going to show that it concerned me. I wore an air of total indifference as I dodged and weaved my way through the crowd.

I expect that, had I not been wearing the stereo, I would have heard some warning - some audible clue that things were about to go horribly wrong. I was in my own little world though – Miss Independent, that's me.

Suddenly the people around me moved away. The crowd thinned and I could actually see where I was putting my feet. I realize now that some people tried to warn me, but I simply ignored everyone. What I could not ignore was the 30-foot-long steel ladder which landed right on top of me. I fell in a crumpled heap.

I came to, on the concrete, with blood oozing from a wound to my head. There were all sorts of noises going on inside my head, then I realized that the stereo was still playing. I tried to move my hands to remove the ear-phones but my arms wouldn't work properly. I was aware of something heavy resting on top of me.

Suddenly it all went quiet. I thought I was dead. It must all go quiet when you die. I could feel someone touching my head. It hurt and I wanted them to stop. I tried to speak but couldn't. I was not dead, but it felt like I was dying.

'It's not fair, I'm still a virgin,' I thought to myself.

I tried to move again. This time I had a little more success. My arm came up against something cold, something metallic. I tried to look at what I had touched and saw that part of a ladder was only inches from my face. I could not move because the ladder was across my body. I closed my eyes and wished someone would move the ladder for me. Then someone tried to move the ladder and it hurt my head. I wished they would leave it alone until I felt a little better. I remembered that it was often considered bad luck to walk under a ladder. Now I knew why.

At that point I must have lost consciousness.

CASE 6: MATTHEW

Matthew is 25, single and a keen sportsman. He works for the education service of a coastal town in California. He has his own modest house and a very active social life. The two events he describes occurred in March 1991 and November 1991.

It was all so unexpected. I wanted to call around and see my friend to discuss the fishing trip we were going to make together at the weekend. I was really looking forward to the peace and quiet of the lake, a few beers, and a good long chat about anything and everything.

There was no answer at the front door, but I could hear the dog barking inside. I had tried ringing a few minutes earlier, but the telephone was engaged. John was in, so why didn't he answer the door?

I went around to the back of the house, and rapped on the door there. The dog still barked, but I didn't hear the approaching footsteps which would have heralded John's arrival at the door. Looking through the window I could see the dog. However, the dog was not looking my way, it was looking into the living room and continuing to bark.

I didn't really like dogs much, and had no great understanding of their habits. (I'm not really keen on any animals.) I did know, though, that when you knocked on a door the dog barked at the door and not into the room away from the door. Something was wrong. Perhaps John was ill. I had to find a way of getting into the house to check that everything was OK.

I started to hunt around for an open window. Nothing. I tried my own keys in the locks without any real expectation that they would work. I was not surprised. I was going to have to break in. I knocked on the door again. The dog continued to bark. The noise was starting to get on my nerves.

Picking up a large stone I smashed it against one of the small panes of glass in the back door. It made a terrible noise and I half expected neighbours to start flooding out of their homes, accusing me of burglary. Reaching inside the smashed window I hunted for the key that should be in the lock on the inside of the door. Finding it at last I unlocked the door, withdrew my hand and tried to open the door. It wouldn't budge.

I remembered that there was a bolt at the top of the door. Smashing another piece of glass I managed to slide back the bolt and the door opened when I tried it for the second time.

Standing in the doorway I waited for the dog to bound up to me. I wished I could remember the creature's name. But he did not come bounding up to me. This made me nervous and, looking around the kitchen, I selected a large sharp knife and, thus armed, I moved cautiously towards the living room.

I don't know what I expected to find exactly, but what I did find took me totally by surprise. John was sitting in his armchair by the fireplace. On the floor beside his chair was a glass and an empty bottle of scotch. His lap was covered in a deep reddish-brown stain. John had cut both his wrists, and had probably done so some hours ago. He was dead.

I rushed to the phone - not that the situation required urgency, but it seemed appropriate at the time. I stopped and stared at the instrument. It was one of those cordless devices that you could take with you as you wander around the house. The handset was missing and two little red lights on the base set were illuminated. I started to hunt for the handset. No wonder I could not get through to John on the phone.

I found the handset on the floor alongside the empty glass by John's chair. As I reached down to pick it up, I realized that I was still holding the kitchen knife I had so bravely armed myself with earlier. Picturing how John had died, I dropped the knife in horror. Slowly backing out of the room, I turned, and rushed out of the back door. I had to find a neighbour and use her phone. I was not looking forward to the next few hours.

It had been some months since John's funeral. My life had returned to normal, although I greatly missed my friend. Returning home from work one day, I noticed that the door to my flat was wide open. Somebody was inside. I walked quietly into the hallway and through to the kitchen. I could hear the noise of cupboards and drawers being opened in the dining room. Somebody was going through my things. Without really thinking, I opened a drawer and took out a kitchen knife to arm myself.

'He might have a gun. The sensible thing to do would be to run,' I told myself. I ignored my own advice. Throwing caution to the wind, I rushed to the dining room door and flung it wide open. A young man looked up from the cupboard he was searching and saw me standing there with the knife raised. A look of panic crossed his face and his eyes darted around the room looking for an escape route.

Suddenly, my mind took me back to John's house and the way I had walked into his living room with a knife raised in the expectation that John was being burgled. Then I could see John sitting in my chair, wrists cut, bleeding all over the floor. I backed into the hall and started to shake violently.

My young burglar couldn't believe his luck. Pushing me backwards, he rushed past me and out of the door. It was some considerable time before I managed to get back on to my feet and close the outside door. What had happened to me?

CASE 7: RICHARD

Aged 41, Richard works as a police officer in an inner city area in Mississippi State. He has three teenage children by his first marriage and had married again in 1987. He has been a police officer for 20 years and has 'seen it all'. The traumatic event occurred in August 1992.

The house was a large terraced property. The basement had grilles over the front and back windows and the door had several locks – safety precautions which are not unusual for the area.

The family of five lived in this basement. There was a history of domestic fights, and recently they had become quite vicious. While the family slept, the door was made secure and the keys thrown from the window.

The children woke to find petrol being poured on them by their father. The basement flat was set alight. A web of fire quickly spread all around the mother and her children. There was no way out of the flat. They smashed the grille-covered windows to get air, and to yell for help.

A family above heard the commotion and raised the alarm. They made an abortive attempt to try to smash the door down, but were beaten by its strength. I was in a passing police car which was flagged down at the end of the block. There was no time to prepare myself, mentally and physically, for what was about to happen in the next few minutes.

Stopping outside the front of the house, I saw the smoke coming from the basement windows. I saw, and heard, the victims as they stood as close to the fresh air as they could get. Red flames flickered behind them. I thought it was a picture of hell with arms waving hopelessly and cries for help.

It became obvious that the door was not going to give way. The people who had been putting their shoulders to it were now getting tired, and were also being affected by the thickening smoke. The area in front of the door was restricted by stairs and rubbish bins. There was not much room in which to work. I ran down the stairway to take over at the door. It appeared hopeless, but I had at least to try. I passed the window and recoiled in horror as arms reached out to try and grab me. I felt sick deep down inside.

I got a lungfull of smoke and that frightened me as I gasped for breath. Looking around, I realized that I was alone at the door. The other people had retreated back up the stairway to the street.

I wanted to leave, but couldn't. I couldn't leave those people to die without hope. I could still see them watching me from the window. I tried the door again, but it held firm. I accepted that I was going to have to watch these people die. There was nothing more I could do.

I saw the mother holding a young boy up to the window trying to give him some air, and to protect him from the fire. The fire was smouldering as there was clearly not a lot of air in the basement. The flames seemed to be like some dark animal in the background. It appeared inevitable that the flames were going to slowly advance towards the window and consume the helpless figures who stood there.

I was unable to speak to them, I felt so helpless. I looked away and swallowed hard. I remembered hearing that it was possible to force a door if you sat on the floor and braced yourself against the opposite wall. My legs were like jelly, but it was worth one last effort before the smoke became too thick.

I decided that I would stay by the door, trying to force it open – until the people inside lost consciousness and disappeared from the window. I did not want them to witness me giving up. I accepted that I might be injured myself, but that those injuries would be slight compared with the suffering inside the basement.

The door gave slightly at the bottom, but then sprang back into place. The whole incident was taking on an air of unreality. Then suddenly the door gave way and opened. I shouted for others to help me. I was unsure what to do next. Should I go inside?

The children came to the front door, followed by

their mother. Now that the door was open, air was rushing into the building and the fire intensified. Flames were now licking around the windows. I told everyone to crouch low, cover their mouths and run up the stairway.

Looking inside the door, I could see a room and a male body on the floor. He was badly burned. I charged inside and grabbed hold of him, but he made no effort to move himself. I managed to drag him towards the door and screamed for others to come and help me. I was scared. The fire was burning fiercely now, the far wall of the room where I stood was like a red waterfall. Another policeman joined me and we half carried, half dragged the person out of the basement. At one point the body fell across the doorway, blocking my exit from the basement. This caused me to panic and scream at him to get up and move. I swore at him repeatedly as I tried to move him outside. At one point I even kicked at him to make him move.

My memory has blanked out some of this struggle, but we managed to get everyone to the top of the stairway where others took over from me. Eventually the fire trucks arrived at the building. By this time the flames were reaching the footpath. The injured were stretched out in the street; there was nowhere for them to go until an ambulance arrived.

I started to feel very weak and sank to the ground. I was unable to act or think clearly any more. I just watched as others ran around me dealing with the injured and the fire. Eventually I was taken to hospital, suffering from 'shock'. There I learned that the man I had half dragged from the basement had died. It was also alleged that he had caused the fire in the first place.

I shed no tears for him.

CASE 8: FELICITY

Felicity was just 13 years old when all this started. At that time, she lived at home with her parents and older brother. She worked well at school and her future looked promising. She loved the quiet Cheshire village in which she lived. Her father had once been prosecuted for drinking and driving. Felicity never forgot the embarrassment of the court case. These events took place between March 1990 and November 1991.

It all started one night when I had a bad dream. I was being arrested for something I didn't do and was putting up a pretty good fight. I awoke from the dream to find myself sitting upright in bed being cuddled by my older brother. He was stroking the back of my head and talking to me in a smooth calm voice.

I pulled back from him a little, then relaxed as I realized what had happened. I must have been calling out in my sleep and, as Mum and Dad were away, Michael had come into my room to see what was the matter.

I relaxed and laid back down on my pillows. Michael smiled and tidied my bed covers. He was 18, five years older than me. We got on well together, however. We seemed to understand each other. He blew me a kiss good-night and left the room.

Three nights later, I woke again to feel somebody beside me. I did not remember having any dream but guessed I must have done. I had been troubled by the same dream (being arrested) quite a bit recently.

Michael was with me again. He was stroking my arm and talking quietly to me. It felt nice and I was not worried in the least. Then he pulled back the covers and slid into bed beside me. I rested my arm across him and drifted back to sleep. When I woke in the morning I was on my own.

The pattern continued for some weeks.

One night in July it was really hot. I could not stand my nightdress sticking to me, so I slept on top of the covers, naked. The sound of the door closing woke me and I saw Michael walk quietly towards my bed. I knew I had not woken him so wondered what the matter was. He stood beside my bed, looking at me and I could just make out his smile. His hand reached down and touched my breast. I turned away and tried to find my quilt to cover me up.

Michael sat on the bed and started to touch me again. I tried to sit up but he pushed me back, quite gently, and put his finger to his lips. I didn't like what he was doing.

Michael stayed with me for some time that night. He hurt me and I felt dirty. In the morning I showered, changed the bedclothes and placed all the dirty laundry in the washing machine before breakfast. I think my parents thought I had wet the bed, but nothing was said. I could not look at Michael when he came down to breakfast. In comparison, he was laughing and fooling around in his usual way just as if nothing had happened.

Michael came to my room quite often after that. I hated him for it, but felt that I was powerless to stop it. I couldn't tell anyone – Michael told me what he would do to me if I ever told. My parents would only argue, and it might be my fault! I started sleeping with my clothes on.

About 18 months later, I was with a group of friends after school. One of them had managed to get hold of some 'stuff' and we had agreed to meet and share it. There were about six of us in a little group when someone shouted 'Police'. I saw the car and started to run. There were only two officers but both appeared to run after me. It was not long before one of them caught hold of my arm and pulled me to a stop. I kicked out at her and tried to scratch. I felt I was fighting for my life.

It was all so much like my dream. The arrest that I had been dreading was now taking place. It was the first time I had been involved with any kind of drugs, and I had been caught. I also had a strange feeling that the woman officer knew all about me and Michael. I was frightened. What were they going to do with me?

CASE 9: PAUL

Paul is 24 and single. He lives in a flat on his own; his last relationship ended when the girl simply moved out. He works for a European Bank and frequently travels between England and the Continent. The event which nearly cost him his life took place in March 1987.

It was March 1987 and I had enjoyed my first trip of the year to the Continent. Everything was as it should be. I was in a great mood and looking forward to the crossing.

It was all so sudden. One minute I was sitting quietly by the window on the right hand side of the ship. I couldn't see much outside because of the way the light caught the glass. There was no hint of trouble. People were all around, talking in excited voices. Smiles and happy faces, that's what I remember.

Then there was a shudder and the ship started to move over to the left. I was rising higher and the people to my left were being lowered. It was an awful sensation. I totally lost my bearings and could not work out what was happening. Then the lights went out. I tumbled out of my seat and fell. I fell for what appeared to be for ever. Then I landed with a thump which knocked all the air out of my body. I didn't move for quite a while. I just lay still, trying to work out exactly what was going on. Was it all some kind of dream, a nightmare?

Something moved underneath me. I was on top of somebody. In fact, I was on top of several people. Someone screamed. That started several others. The air filled with screams and shouts. I was travelling on my own, so had nobody to shout to. That didn't stop me calling out for help.

Above the noise of the shouting were all sorts of other strange noises. Creaks and groans that I could not identify. Then I realized what it was. The ship must have struck something, or run aground, and we were sinking. The ship had turned on to its side, throwing me from my seat, and we were going to sink.

I panicked. What could we do? What could I do? Were we going to die? Would anyone rescue us? I recalled films of sea disasters and reminded myself to stay calm. If the ship turned over, there would still be air inside it and we would be rescued by somebody. That's what happened in the films. But in the films, sometimes the passengers died. The panic intensified.

I started to climb up. I could not see much, but my eyes were slowly getting used to the gloom. I climbed on to the edge of a seat, and then on to the seat above that. The ship was at an angle of about 60 degrees and the angle was growing steadily steeper. Climbing up the seats was becoming more and more difficult.

Others started to climb, too. Some complained of pains in arms, legs and chests. Clearly there had already been some injuries, maybe even some deaths. I started to feel guilty about the person I had fallen upon. He had not spoken, or moved. Perhaps I had knocked him unconscious when I landed so heavily upon him.

The voices quietened, people started to breathe more heavily as they clambered over the ship's furniture. One or two called out to their family. Some sobbed to themselves. It just didn't feel real.

The ship shuddered again suddenly. One or two people fell again. There was a scream to one side of me. Water was coming into the cabin. I could hear it clearly. I started to climb again. I had to get as far away from the water as I could. I think I was close to an exit when someone pulled me backwards and pushed past me. I fell to the floor once again.

I have no real memory of what happened next. I somehow found myself sitting in a helicopter. I was soaked to the skin and had what turned out to be a badly broken arm. Sitting beside me was a woman with a nasty cut on her forehead. We were both shivering despite the warm blankets we had been given. I couldn't believe that I was safe. I later learned that 192 people had died in the ship or in the sea nearby.

CASE 10: CHRISTINE

Christine is 37 years old, married with two daughters. She

lives with her family in a smart, detached house on the south Devonshire coast. She works as an architect for a large partnership, and has just been made a junior partner in the firm. She has a company car, and is developing a successful career. The event she describes took place in September 1991.

This is not an easy story for me to tell. I considered myself to be a modern liberated woman. Not a feminist, not a sexist, but good at my job, and usually able to handle most people and situations which presented themselves. Consequently, this experience has totally wrecked my self-confidence, and my control over my life.

It was quite late in the day, and I had just one more call to make. I was visiting a doctor's surgery. One of the doctors was opening a new practice and I was designing the premises for him. I had built up a good working relationship with the doctors and had already attended several meetings at the old surgery. This last visit had been rearranged, but I saw nothing unusual in that I was expected to call at the surgery outside normal hours. Many doctors preferred to see 'non-patients' at that particular time of the day. This fitted in with their pattern of house calls and other commitments.

The front door to the surgery was unlocked and I could see a few lights on. The early evening sun was starting to fade and I felt slightly chilly in just my skirt and blouse. Once inside the building, it was easy to follow the signs to the doctor's consulting room. I made a mental note to discuss signing for the new building. The door was ajar, but from force of habit, I swapped my briefcase to my left hand and tapped on the door with my right.

The door opened abruptly and a smiling face appeared. Initially, I took a brief step back. The suddenness had momentarily startled me. However, I quickly regained my composure and returned the smile. Introductions were unnecessary as we had met on at least six previous occasions.

'Come in, come in, take your clothes off!'

'Pardon me?'

'Sorry. Little joke there. I'm off on holiday tomorrow, so I'm feeling a little light-hearted and happy just now. Would you like a drink?'

'A coffee would be wonderful, thank you.'

'I was thinking of something with a little more life in it.'

'In that case, I think I'll take a rain check on that. I have to drive home later.'

I should have realized at this point that it was not going to be a standard meeting, but I guessed that a doctor about to go off on holiday was entitled to feel a little relief at the prospect and, in consequence, be a little less official than I would usually expect.

Sitting down, I noticed that I was being given the 'once-over'. His gaze was definitely somewhere between hip and knee. I recrossed my legs, smoothing my skirt tidily to just above my knees, and tried to put any silly thoughts out of my mind. This man was a doctor after all.

I opened my briefcase and pulled out a bundle of papers I didn't really need, but felt more confident with them in my hand. I asked if he had the financial calculations ready for me.

'All in good time, all in good time.' There was that

smile again. He pulled his chair a little closer and rubbed his hands together. Then he placed one on my knee. Inside I shuddered, but managed to smile and gently remove his hand while I uncrossed and recrossed my legs. I turned my body slightly towards the door.

'Actually, I'm a little pushed for time, so if you don't have the figures ready, perhaps I could call back for them some other time?'

'No. No, they are here. I'll just have to find them for you, Christine.'

He stood and wandered over to the filing cabinet by the door. I started to return the papers to my briefcase but the door slamming shut made me jump and some of the papers spilled on to the floor. Looking up, I saw him standing in front of the now-closed door, still with that awful smile - sort of menacing.

'Let's stop mucking about, shall we? You agreed to come here at this time. What did you expect?'

My skin started to crawl. The hairs at the back of my neck tingled. The penny had dropped. What a fool I had been. In a rush, I jammed the rest of the papers into my briefcase and stood up. I had to leave as quickly as possible. This had gone far enough.

I tried to dodge around the outstretched arms but couldn't avoid them in the confines of the room. He pulled me towards him and tried to kiss me. Turning away, I started to call out but his hand clamped over my mouth and he pushed me backwards. The smile had vanished. His face was shiny with perspiration. His eyes had a cold look about them. His free hand started to roam over my body.

I don't know where I got the strength from, but my knee came up and he jumped backwards to avoid it. I broke free, only to feel a sharp pain in my stomach as a punch took all my breath away.

'That's the way it's going to be is it, Christine?'

'Let me go now, and that will be the end of it.'

'Oh no.' He moved forward again. 'I'm going to have you, Christine. You know you want it, too. Either way, though, I'm stronger than you, and the building is empty. Nobody will hear.'

He moved forward and grabbed me again. The full realization of his words made me turn cold. There was little I could do. I had never felt so helpless in my life. I looked around for a weapon, but the room was too tidy. There was nothing for me to use.

I could feel the wall behind me. My back was pressed against it as he came forward again. In one sudden lunge he was pressed against me, his mouth searching for mine as I struggled to pull away. I could feel his hands on me, freeing my clothing. I felt angry, sick, disgusted and cross with myself, although I still could not understand how I could possibly have given all the signals which had led to this situation developing.

It was almost 20 minutes before I could escape from that room. I must have looked a complete wreck as I ran from the building to the side street where I had parked my car. Locking myself in the vehicle I closed my eyes and tried to block out the memory of what had happened. But even with my eyes tightly shut I could still see that awful grin.

How could I possibly tell anyone what had happened to me?

Summary of the 10 illustrated cases

Case	Name	Age	Incident	Occupation
1	David	35	Physically assaulted, beaten	Police Officer
2	Marlene	43	Innocent party in two motoring accidents	Nurse
3	Jessica	30	Experienced very traumatic Caesarean section	Shop assistant
4	Graham	48	Brick thrown through his car window	Fire Officer
5	Cindy	19	Hit by falling ladder	Student
6	Matthew	25	Discovered suicide of friend, then burgled	Educationalist
7	Richard	41	Witnessed house fire, people trapped	Police Officer
8	Felicity	13	Sexually abused by brother	Schoolgirl
9	Paul	24	Rescued from sinking ship	Bank clerk
10	Christine	37	Raped by a doctor	Architect

Chapter three

Symptoms

Part of the counselling process is to look at what symptoms are being suffered and to explain the messages that the body and mind are sending. Symptoms of PTSD fall into three broad groups: intrusive, avoidant and physical. Taken individually, some symptoms may appear to be simply minor irritations with no cause for concern. Taken in combination, these same symptoms can totally destroy lifestyle, partnerships and homes.

Untreated, these symptoms can last a lifetime. It is therefore vital that the symptoms are seen for what they are: the natural consequence of being confronted with a traumatic, life-threatening event. The three types of symptom are linked closely to the diagnostic table describing PTSD. (See page 6.)

Five criteria need to be met before a diagnosis of Post-Traumatic Stress Disorder can be made.[1]

---

        1 The person must have witnessed or experienced a serious threat (real or perceived) to his life or physical well-being.

INTRUSIVE 2 The person must re-experience the event, or part of the event, in some form.

AVOIDANT	3	The person must persistently avoid situations associated with the trauma, or experience a numbing of general responsiveness.
PHYSICAL	4	The person must experience persistent symptoms of increased arousal, or 'over-awareness'.
	5	Symptoms must have lasted at least a month.

Not everyone who experiences the first four criteria will be troubled by the symptoms for over a month. It is only those who continue to suffer after that period who can truly be confirmed as suffering from Post-Traumatic Stress Disorder.

If the disorder is successfully treated within six months, it is described as an acute case of PTSD. Over half of those initially affected have recovered three months later and can therefore be defined as acute PTSD sufferers.

When the condition persists for more than six months, it is a case of chronic PTSD. In these instances, the 'trauma beliefs' have become less susceptible to influence, repeated avoidance behaviour is well established, and sufferers are far more likely to default from counselling. Consequently, the chronic condition is often compounded by feelings of depression and anxiety, and treatment becomes more difficult.

When a person encounters a traumatic, life-threatening event, the brain juggles between recalling the painfulness of the event (intrusions) and going to great lengths to forget it (avoidance). The sufferer's mood will see-saw between the two. Each process has its own set of symptoms which, in turn, act as a catalyst for the physical symptoms to develop.

There are 17 main symptoms of Post-Traumatic Stress Disorder. Not all are experienced by every sufferer.

INTRUSIVE	– Recurrent and distressing recollections – flashbacks, thoughts, nightmares, dreams. – Phobias, about specific daily routines, events or objects. – Feelings of guilt for having survived.
AVOIDANT	– Detachment from others, emotional numbness. – Avoidance of thoughts or feelings associated with the event. – Markedly diminished interest or pleasure in most activities.
PHYSICAL	– Sleep problems. – Irrational or impulsive behaviour. – Increased irritability. – Impaired memory. – Inability to concentrate. – Hypervigilance. – Exaggerated startle response. – Violent outbursts. – Joint/muscle pains. – Feelings of nervousness.
CO-EXISTENT	– Depression/anxiety

INSTRUSIVE SYMPTOMS

The person must re-experience the event, or part of the event, in some form.
The three main intrusive symptoms of PTSD are recurrent and distressing recollections (flashbacks, thoughts, nightmares and dreams), phobias about specific daily routines, events or objects, and feelings of guilt for having survived. Every sufferer will be experiencing at least one of these three symptoms.

The flashbacks operate like a camera within the mind. During the incident, photographs of the trauma are stored away in the recesses of memory. These photographs are reproduced before the victim's eyes in graphic detail. They can appear at any time of the day, often without warning, instantly transporting the sufferer to the heart of the trauma, just as if it were happening again.

The depth of detail within these flashbacks can be both fascinating and terrifying for those who experience them. John Le Carré writes in his novel *Tinker, Tailor, Soldier, Spy*: 'There are moments which are made up of too much stuff for them to be lived at the time they occur.'

It is these moments which are reproduced as very vivid flashbacks.

Jessica:
I was out shopping and I suddenly felt that the shop was very crowded. I froze.

I could see myself waiting to go into the operating theatre. I was looking down on myself. It was all so real. I couldn't get the picture out of my mind. I could almost reach out and touch myself.

It was over as suddenly as it started. I then felt very foolish and imagined everyone in the store to be looking at me. I had to abandon my shopping and leave.

Besides these flashbacks, sufferers may frequently be troubled by thoughts and memories of the trauma. These thoughts may be along the lines of 'what if?' or 'if only', and can be a source of both anxiety and depression. Unlike the flashbacks, thoughts are conscious and can be controlled by the sufferer. Distractions can take one's mind away from these troublesome thoughts.

Dreams and nightmares can be extremely distressing. Like the flashbacks, there is little or no control over them. They creep up subconsciously and disturb any sleep the sufferer manages to achieve. Nightmares can be extremely vivid, and often focus on just one or two aspects of the trauma - those which are causing the sufferer most anguish. The nightmares can often become so violent that it would be unsafe for partners to share the same bed for fear of being unintentionally injured by thrashing arms and legs. Being woken from such frantic nightmares is often necessary, but can also be very distressing for the sufferer. The more frequent the nightmares are, the less inclined the sufferer becomes to want to go to sleep. This lack of restful sleep only compounds other problems such as mood and irritability.

Victims often suffer from feelings of grief and guilt. The guilt is linked to survival while the grief is linked to loss. The loss need not necessarily be loss of life. The loss could be of property (natural disaster), virginity (incest or rape), or integrity and self-esteem (assault). These losses are all sources of grief and can be compounded if the sufferer also loses his job as a consequence of his suffering. In each of these instances the grief is as real, and as natural as bereavement.

The guilt about survival is equally natural. If the trauma resulted in other people's deaths, it is likely that survivors will be asking themselves why they deserved to survive while others perished. They feel guilty that some element of good fortune or quick thinking saved them from death, but did not save people who may have been standing alongside them a few moments before the tragedy struck. Such guilt can lead to feelings of unworthiness and embarrassment at having survived.

The third intrusive symptom of PTSD is the suffering from phobias about specific daily routines, events or objects. In truth, the word *phobia* should not be applied here. The symptom would be more correctly described as avoidance behaviour. A phobia is 'an abnormal intense and irrational fear of a given situation, organism or object'. The fears experienced by PTSD sufferers are the normal and quite rational responses to a traumatic event. Whatever the differences in the definitions of phobias and avoidance behaviours, the actual consequences of either condition are, in essence, the same: a terrifying fear of something.[2]

If you place your finger over a flame, you will burn it. Therefore people do not, generally, go around putting their fingers into flames - they avoid this activity. In the same way, if you were trapped in a lift with a person who raped you at knife-point, it would be quite natural for you to always choose to use the stairs in the future. You avoid the lift because it is explicitly linked to the trauma. You also have a fear that the lift might halt between floors again and that the whole traumatic incident could be repeated. The longer you avoid lifts, the more difficult it becomes to enter one. Eventually, the fear of entering a lift may become even greater than the fear of being raped as proved by the fact that other potential rape locations are not avoided, but you would not even enter a lift with your own mother.

Some objects or activities can act as a trigger and induce flashbacks of the trauma. After five years as a hostage, during which he was bound with masking tape every time he was moved from cell to cell, it is not surprising that Terry Waite intensely dislikes the sound of masking tape being ripped from its roll. The sound triggers memories of his imprisonment. In such circumstances it would be quite natural to avoid ever using masking tape again. Staples and glue are available as alternative fixers, so why use tape? Such action would be seen by some as a phobic reaction to rolls of masking tape. In fact, it is *avoidance* of the tape because it invokes so many bad memories.

In some situations, the avoidance behaviour can dominate daily life. Fear of travelling in cars or on public transport can be very restricting. Fear of crowds, telephones, stairs, lifts, and many other objects or situations can soon start to dominate and restrict the victim's life.

AVOIDANT SYMPTOMS

The person must persistently avoid situations associated with the trauma, or experience a numbing of responsiveness.
The three primary avoidant symptoms of PTSD are a detachment from others and emotional numbness, an avoidance of thoughts or feelings associated with the event and a markedly diminished interest or pleasure in most

activities. Every sufferer will be experiencing one or more of these three symptoms.

Many PTSD sufferers feel that the emotional side of their character make-up has let them down. Somehow they have become over-emotional. To compensate for this, they start to switch off their emotions and feelings towards others. This feels like the safe option and a sensible thing to do.

Graham:
I spend much of my day at home, alone. My wife is out at work during the week. At weekends I like to go swimming, or walking, or cycling. Basically, I like to do things that involve me being on my own. That way there are no awkward questions. I don't have to think about anything complicated - I just drift. I don't think I even enjoy the exercise.

If I was a car, I would be coasting down the road out of gear. I wouldn't turn left or right, I'd just travel on, and on, and on.

The result of this emotional 'switch-off' is that the victim will avoid crowds, avoid friends, avoid fun, and avoid all the things that make life enjoyable. It all becomes too much effort and too risky. It is much safer to curl up and watch the world go by, paint a watery smile on your face, and feel nothing inside. This is known as the numbing phase of PTSD. It is a period of detachment and isolation which has to be broken.

PTSD sufferers also try to avoid any thoughts which might be associated with the trauma in any way. This includes an avoidance of anything that could serve as a reminder of the event and bring an unwanted return of the painful and very intrusive recollections of the trauma.

No medical genius is required to realize that there is a

very thin dividing line between what is an avoidant symptom of PTSD and what is an intrusive symptom of the condition. Many of the resulting behaviour patterns, it could be argued, put some symptoms into both categories. As PTSD is such a personal condition, unique in every case, this confusion in clarifying the symptoms just compounds the complex issues which already exist for the sufferer.

One thing is sure, whether it is an intrusive symptom, or an avoidant symptom, it is very likely that its consequences will leave the sufferer with numerous other physical symptoms.

PHYSICAL SYMPTOMS

The person must experience persistent symptoms of increased arousal, or 'over-awareness'.
Much of the medical focus in the treatment of PTSD has been on the first two groups of symptoms. Yet, it is often the physical symptoms of the condition which are the easiest to detect. If they are traced back to the cause, a diagnosis can be made.

Possibly the first symptoms to be observed in PTSD sufferers are the physical symptoms. Victims go to their doctor with what is called a 'disguised presentation'.[3] There is no deceit intended, it is simply a fact of life that physical symptoms are more noticeable than emotional symptoms and so it is with these physical problems that PTSD sufferers present themselves in the doctor's surgery. There are several common physical PTSD symptoms which are usually products of the earlier onset of avoidant or intrusive symptoms. It is often the development of a physical symptom which brings the condition to the attention of others.

The ten most common physical symptoms are sleep problems; irrational or impulsive behaviour; increased irritability; impaired memory; inability to concentrate; hypervigilance; exaggerated startle response; violent outbursts; joint/muscle pains and feelings of nervousness.

Many PTSD sufferers first present themselves before their family doctor with the complaint that they cannot sleep. All of a sudden the world has started to revolve around this sleep issue; it dominates daily living.

Cindy:
I was getting very bad tempered. I was tired and suffered with frequent headaches. I thought the bump on the head had upset my ability to sleep. I was always wide awake by 4 a.m. In the end I became obsessed with not sleeping. It dominated my thoughts. I blamed everything on being tired and not sleeping very well. I even got a new bed!

If sleep is a problem for you, ask yourself the following six questions:

1 Are you having difficulty in
  getting to sleep?   YES/NO
2 Do you go off to sleep all right
  and wake in the night?   YES/NO
  If YES, after how long?
3 Are you able to get back to sleep?   YES/NO
4 Do you remember dreaming?   YES/NO
5 Do you have nightmares?   YES/NO
6 Are you sleeping too much
  (for example, during the day)?   YES/NO

The answers to these questions will help assess your individual sleep pattern and see how it differs from the way things used to be. This information will be of use to your doctor, too. Many PTSD sufferers have a disturbed sleep pattern and experience problems, both with falling asleep and staying asleep. Paradoxically, a small number of PTSD sufferers have described how difficult they find it to stay awake. Some sufferers are sleeping for 12 or even more hours a day.

Sleep problems can be very stressful. The link between poor quality of sleep and suffering with PTSD is rarely explored in texts about Post-Traumatic Stress Disorder.[4] Yet the link is so obvious.

PTSD sufferers often tend to suffer with bouts of irrational or compulsive behaviour. They can also suffer from increased irritability, especially anger and depression. All this can place intolerable pressures upon relationships.

Christine:
I just exploded. All that happened was that my eldest daughter smashed a plate while washing-up. It was the last straw. I went on and on at her for being so stupid. My husband intervened and tried to take hold of me by the shoulder. I swung around and hit him, hard, across the face.

We stood looking at each other for a few seconds, then I collapsed in floods of tears. Such a simple accident had become a major conflict. It was out of all proportion.

Because PTSD sufferers have experienced a traumatic and potentially life-threatening situation, quite naturally, it has caused them to re-assess their own values. People who were once very thrifty and prudent see little point in saving for the rainy day they might never live to enjoy.

They develop a foreshortened expectation of life, and adjust their living habits accordingly. Their actions appear to be irrational, their attitudes alter. The trauma has, temporarily, altered their character.

When challenged about their change in behaviour, sufferers often become angry; they feel their judgement is no longer trusted. They see the situation as everyone else having changed. This crisis requires careful counselling.

Many PTSD sufferers have difficulty concentrating and remembering things. There is so much going on inside their minds that it should be of little surprise to anyone that memory and concentration should be a problem. Liken it to a computer – when near to saturation point, memory almost full, the computer slows down, its power to operate efficiently has gone. Like the computer, the mind requires time to store away all this new information, and until it is stored away, the operation of thought and memory processes will remain slow.

The effect of this loss of memory and concentration can be most embarrassing. Embarrassing not only for the PTSD sufferer, but for friends and colleagues as they watch the mental torture taking place. Victims can be deep in conversation, then pause – losing track of what they were saying. They might pause to search for the correct word, which totally eludes them.

Whilst driving, sufferers have been known to come to a stop at a green light! They may lose their sense of direction, and be unable to drive to a location they have visited many times before.

Simple mathematical tasks may be totally beyond the concentrational powers of a PTSD sufferer. A simple test used by some medical boards to illustrate this lack of concentration is to count backwards in groups of three, starting from 100.

In combination, the loss of memory and concentration can be terrifying. Simple tasks become ordeals and every day routines become nightmarishly difficult.

Matthew:
All I wanted to do was to use the video recorder. Simple really. There were two programmes I wanted to watch and I had to set the video to record one of them.

It was a nightmare. I couldn't remember how to set the machine. Then I couldn't find a tape with any free space. Finally, when I started to look up the programme times in the listings, I couldn't remember what it was I wanted to record.

I remember thinking, 'This is what it must be like going mad!'

Hypervigilance and an exaggerated startle response are two symptoms which most PTSD sufferers complain of. Both are strongly linked to the experiencing of a serious, life-threatening, traumatic event. When faced with the original traumatic event, the brain responded by increasing the neurotransmitters within the nervous system. To explain it simply: by producing increased quantities of certain chemicals within the nervous system, the brain ensures that the body can fend for itself to its absolute limits.

Having once received these chemical messages during the traumatic event, it appears that the brain is extremely alert and waiting for similar messages. This state of hyper-alertness or hypervigilance means that the sufferer's body is constantly expecting to be faced with a serious 'flight or fight' type of situation. Being constantly at this state of alertness is extremely taxing, and a great strain on the nervous system. Sufferers are constantly assessing and re-assessing their situation. They are looking for the slightest sign that another traumatic incident is about to snare them. The senses of sight and hearing work overtime as they constantly search for signs of danger.

The result of being hypervigilant is that you are ready for absolutely nothing. Your defence system is drained to a point of near exhaustion and you have little or no energy reserves for either 'flight' or 'fight'. Consequently, when something does happen, it frightens the sufferer out of all proportion. The sudden closing of a door, a gentle hand touching your shoulder, a call from a friend; any of these can startle you so much that you jump, gasp for breath and start to panic momentarily. This very exaggerated response to a minor incident probably appears to amuse those around you. After a few moments you may also see the funny side of it all and laugh with them. But, for a few moments, you were terrified. Repeated testing of this exaggerated startle response is exhausting, both physically and emotionally.

Leading on from the hypervigilance and the exaggerated startle response is the likelihood of violent outbursts. Being continually 'hyped-up' and ready for action is not a very secure feeling. Something has to give eventually. Sometimes what gives is the victim's temper; a few seconds of violence that is often totally out of character, and which takes everyone by surprise. What was a friendly party can turn into a fight. A quiet family evening can become a raging, hurtful, row.

Something snaps inside. Maybe something has happened or been said which fires memories of the trauma. Occasionally the trigger can be a smell; a particular type of lighting effect; a household object. It can be something so ordinary that nobody else would ever associate it with a traumatic event. The PTSD victim has made the connection, however, and has acted rashly, violently and defensively in order to prevent any trauma being repeated. Occasionally, such violent outbursts have resulted in PTSD sufferers being prosecuted by the courts.

The final pair of symptoms to fall into this group are the feelings of nervousness and the physical aches and pains experienced by PTSD sufferers. In many cases, it is the continual tension and stressful existence which brings about the nervousness, and in turn brings on cramp, muscle pains and pain in the arm and leg joints.

These pains can be so severe that only strong pain-killing tablets are able to dull them. There is nothing phantom about the pain. It is real enough. The pain is brought about by tense limbs and muscles. The cure is to relax. Such an easy thing to say. Yet it often appears impossible to achieve.

There are other conditions which often exist together with Post-Traumatic Stress Disorder. It is a continuing debate as to whether they are symptoms of the condition or just co-existing. They are depression and anxiety.

Richard:
I found I lost confidence in myself. I felt that I was not able to talk about the event to anyone. Really talk, I mean. I could not admit that I was suffering, and so I suffered in silence. Eventually, I had to seek help from a counselling service, and my self-esteem really hit rock bottom. I was moody, lonely, and sick of everything.

The counsellor mentioned that I was becoming depressed. That thought terrified me. Was I suicidal? Was I in control of myself?

Depression is the ultimate in loneliness.

It is quite possible for someone to suffer with PTSD without feeling depressed. Equally, it is well known that people suffer with depression whilst they have never experienced the trauma of a life-threatening event. However, it is true that those who suffer from chronic PTSD often suffer with bouts of depression and anxiety, too.

PTSD victims often find it easy to hide their feelings. Consequently, there are frequently discrepancies between their behaviour at any medical interview and reports of their moods in the presence of others, especially at home with intimate family and friends.

The following table for self-assessment, if answered honestly, may provide a guide to whether or not your own Post-Traumatic Stress Disorder is compounded by feelings of irritability, depression or anxiety.

Answer the questions, which are divided into three groups of five. Then total your score within each group. The first questions (1-5) deal with feelings of depression. The second group (6-10) look at anxiety, and the third (11-15) irritability. Your score will range between zero and 15 within each group. Any group score over eight may indicate the presence of depression, anxiety or irritability within your present mood swings.

Some counsellors will argue that a pure case of PTSD is something of a rarity, as it so often occurs in conjunction with anxiety and depression. However, when looking at the typical feelings associated with these two disorders, the similarity between the feelings, behaviours and reactions of PTSD sufferers and those of depressed/anxious people are seen as almost indistinguishable.

Typical feelings, behaviour and reactions associated with anxiety and depression.

	Depression	Anxiety
Feelings	Sadness	Apprehension
Behaviour	Indecisiveness Procrastination Poor concentration	Avoidance 'Phobic' fears Dependency
Reactions	Sleeping difficulties Early awakening	Tension Palpitations

TIME SCALE

Symptoms must have lasted at least a month.
Most people who experience a traumatic, potentially life-threatening event will experience some degree of Post-Trauma Stress.[6] It may only last a few hours. It might last days or even weeks. It is ONLY those cases where the post-trauma stress symptoms have stayed with the sufferer for more than one month that can accurately be described as cases of Post-Traumatic Stress Disorder (PTSD).

Table for self-assessment of mood and irritability[5]

	Score			Score
1 I feel cheerful			**2 My appetite is:**	
Yes, definitely	0		Very poor	3
Yes, sometimes	1		Fairly good	2
No, not much	2		Quite good	1
No, not at all	3		Very good	0
3 I have kept up my old interests			**4 I can laugh**	
Yes, most of them	0		Yes, definitely	0
Yes, some of them	1		Yes, sometimes	1
No, not many	2		No, not much	2
No, none of them	3		No, not at all	3
5 I'm awake before I need to get up:				
For 3 hours or more	3			
For 1½ hours or more	2			
For less than 45 minutes	1			
Not at all	0			
6 I can easily sit and relax			**7 I panic for no good reason**	
Yes, definitely	0		Yes, definitely	3
Yes, sometimes	1		Yes, sometimes	2
No, not much	2		No, not much	1
No, not at all	3		No, not at all	0
8 I feel tense or 'worked-up'			**9 I suffer with 'butterfly stomach'**	
Yes, definitely	3		Yes, definitely	3
Yes, sometimes	2		Yes, sometimes	2
No, not much	1		No, not much	1
No, not at all	0		No, not at all	0
10 I can go out alone without feeling anxious				
Yes, always	0			
Yes, sometimes	1			
No, not often	2			
No, I never can	3			
11 I lose my temper and snap at others			**12 I am patient with other people**	
Yes, definitely	3		All of the time	0
Yes, sometimes	2		Most of the time	1
No, not much	1		Some of the time	2
No, not at all	0		Hardly ever	3
13 I feel I might lose control and hit or hurt someone			**14 People upset me and I feel like slamming doors or banging about**	
Sometimes	3		Yes, often	3
Occasionally	2		Yes, sometimes	2
Rarely	1		Only occasionally	1
Never	0		Not at all	0
15 Lately, I have been getting annoyed with myself				
Very much so	3			
Rather a lot	2			
Not much	1			
Not at all	0			

Chapter four

◄○►

Families and friends

At the centre of any traumatic incident are the victims and the rescuers. These people are surrounded by a network of family and friends. It follows, therefore, that those are also going to be affected by the traumatic incident. They become secondary victims of Post-Traumatic Stress Disorder.

PARTNERS

Like bereavement, traumatic responses can have both positive and negative consequences. Some couples will be drawn closer together. They will share the concerns and worries of their partners. Their need for each other will deepen. Other couples may find themselves drifting apart, maybe searching for a less demanding and more shallow relationship. Recovery from PTSD is a painful experience for all of them.

Whichever way you look at the situation, the partners of PTSD sufferers are in for a difficult time. There are few short cuts and plenty of rows, interspersed with occasional successes.

The relationship can feel very uneasy because life has suddenly shown how unpredictable it can be. In the aftermath of the trauma this is quite understandable, and allowances can be made for the erratic mood of the victim. With time, however, the level of understanding can diminish, and what was originally considered to be erratic behaviour becomes misinterpreted as sheer bloody-mindedness.

A reluctance to discuss things can become a source of friction in a relationship. It is often the case that PTSD sufferers are unwilling to discuss the trauma with their partner, but are more inclined to impart the details to friends. Such behaviour might be mistaken for a lack of trust, but it is more to do with protecting those closest to them. Some victims have found that they can sit in the local bar and tell friends how close they came to death, but would be totally unable to relate the same story at home, alone, with their partner. This 'protection' of the partner is very common and lasts only a short time in most cases. However, it does give rise to feelings of rejection. The partner feels excluded from some part of the loved-one's life. *Do not* put undue pressure on your partner to tell everything in one go. You will get the full story, but it might be delivered in small, more manageable chapters.

Money can be a source of constant anxiety and worry. Many PTSD victims are unable to work for a long period of time. This lack of employment will inevitably be reflected in financial straits within the family. In these cases, money is a frequent topic of conversation, and a constant reminder that all is not well. Financial problems bring pressure to return to work quickly. Often this can force a premature return to work with the inevitable consequence that more time off work will be required at a later date. State benefits, company welfare, and insurance policies can lessen the financial blow to many families, but the problem never really goes away.

Sex often becomes an issue between partners. Either one or both can discover an increased or decreased physical desire. On top of all the other changes going on at the time, this variation in sexual appetite will be an added strain. Partners may start to search for a reason for this change and there may be feelings of insecurity as the change is inflicted upon the relationship very speedily. Worries about sexual faithfulness may grow if partners find themselves becoming sexually incompatible. This all adds up to increased strain at a time when the relationship needs a little extra flexibility.

It is difficult to maintain a close personal relationship when your thoughts are constantly interrupted by images of a life-threatening, traumatic situation. Many veterans of war have found it almost impossible to remain in such a relationship while continuing to mourn the deaths of those colleagues who were close to them. It is important to take professional advice before the changes inflicted by the trauma impose an irreversible situation.

Jessica:
I knew the wives of several war veterans. They told me that their husbands occasionally just shut them out of their lives. They would drift off into their own thoughts and totally ignore the family around them.

I realized that that is how I felt sometimes. I had never been anywhere near a war, but my feelings were very similar to the veterans. I wanted to be alone. I didn't want to be touched or cuddled. I didn't want to talk. I just shut my husband out.

With so much changing, panic is quite a natural reaction. In the case of PTSD victims and their partners, this may show itself as bouts of excessive spending. When a life-plan has suddenly been totally turned upside-down it can lead to feelings of 'let's spend, and enjoy it while we can'. Although the occasional treat is fully justified, squandering life savings in a matter of weeks is invariably a great mistake. Such whims, which will only add further difficulties to the process of recovery from the trauma, must be guarded against.

Another issue which is likely to unsettle partners is a change in lifestyle. A partnership may develop a new approach, perhaps with the other partner taking the lead. This can be a simple matter of who drives the car, or it might be that the role of major bread-winner has passed from one partner to the other. This new way of life, or new image may take time to adapt to. There may be conflicts within the partnership, particularly when the victim wishes to regain control over aspects of life which had temporarily become the responsibility of the other partner.

This situation may build up all sorts of anger and frustration which can be directed at anything or anyone when the explosion finally comes. Both partners must be made aware of what is taking place.

The inability to make even the simplest decisions can become infuriating. Constant preoccupation with the incident, the keeping of scrap books and diaries, can appear to be shutting the other partner out of this part of life.

Changes in mood can often catch partners out. Moods may suddenly swing from contentedness to disorientated confusion, then to total loss of interest in a very short space of time. Nightmares and dreams can also be very disturbing for partners.

Shame and fear about behaviour, plus avoidance of

anything to do with the incident can drastically restrict family life. Activities which were once very popular may suddenly become a thing of the past.

Graham:

Things that I used to think important have lost that importance in my life. My car needed new tyres. I knew that it was risky driving on the existing set, but I just didn't care. I drove around for about three months like that. Every time I saw a police car I felt guilty, but I still did not change them.

Eventually my wife noticed them. I got a real earful from her for not doing anything about it. I just threw her the keys and told her to do it herself. That sort of thing had always been one of my jobs around the house.

She just stared at me, walked out and slammed the door. I watched her drive down the road with tears running down her cheeks. I felt terrible about it.

When she returned we had a cuddle and I said how sorry I was. She explained that she had actually quite enjoyed her change in role. Going to the garage and pricing a set of tyres was a new experience for her.

CHILDREN AND PARENTS

It is sometimes impossible for children to express their feelings about a traumatic event. That does not mean they are unaffected. Adults frequently underestimate a child's level of understanding of complicated issues. This underestimation is a positive hindrance when assessing how children have been affected by a family trauma (see Chapter 8).

Added to this complication is the child's natural inquisitiveness and ability to catch snatches of adult conversations. In consequence, the child may perceive the trauma to be even more dramatic than it already is. The truth may hurt initially, but in the long term a policy of honesty is more likely to ease the situation.

'Daddy's not very well' or 'Mummy's had a bit of a shock' are not adequate explanations for adults. Why should they be adequate for children?

Matthew:
Working with children for most of the day, I have come to understand just how tough they are. Many of them wanted to talk about death. Most had experienced someone close to them dying.

Following John's death, I found that I had developed a greater understanding of what these children had been telling me. I realized that their perception of death, and its consequences, was often very mature.

I never actually told them about John's death. That would not have been right. But I think they sensed that I really did understand what they were telling me.

However, some issues are beyond the comprehension of very young children. The trauma of being raped means very little to a three-year-old. In such situations, a simplified version of the trauma must be prepared. Not a lie, but a simple version of the truth.

HOW DO CHILDREN COPE?

Children don't sit down and talk about their worries and troubles. They incorporate their fears into their play and their attitudes to others. They may become uncharacteristically aggressive towards their peers. Their games may develop themes which involve conflict and aggression: war games, criminal actions or violent accidents may all be acted out. The aggression may become explosive in nature, making the child unpopular at a time when friends are necessary.

Child primary victims of PTSD tend to show fear and are easily startled. They have a very disturbed sleep pattern and exhibit signs of guilt and depression. Occasionally these children will switch off, becoming disengaged from their surroundings, and their return to the present may precipitate an act of aggression.

Children who become secondary victims of PTSD, because of a traumatic event experienced by a close family member, may well experience the same symptoms.

Because of the difficulty in establishing support groups for child PTSD sufferers, it is frequently very hard to set up satisfactory counselling for these young victims of trauma.

The parents of PTSD victims also have a tough time. This includes both parents of young victims and parents of adult PTSD sufferers. In many families the parent-child bond remains close. In others, the trauma may drive a wedge clean through that close bond. An uneasiness develops in the relationship. Things become less easy to talk about. Silences become strained. In these instances, somebody must take the lead. The PTSD victim should be given every opportunity to talk, but should not be coerced into talking. It is quite natural for the victim to wish to protect parents from the awful reality of what has happened. Viewed from the parents' side, this may feel like being shut out, and it may hurt. Opportunities to discuss the trauma and the fears should be provided. Once the victim starts to talk, there will probably be no stopping them, but it may be some time before the moment feels right. Patience is required.

FRIENDS AND WORKMATES

PTSD can stretch friendship to the very limit. It is a difficult time for the friends and colleagues of a victim. They feel that they must do something, but find that when they cannot do anything there is an overwhelming sense of failure. Friends are not usually trained in counselling, but they already have the trust and friendship of the victim. In these circumstances, it is not surprising that many victims find it easier to talk to a friend in a way that they have been unable to talk to partners and close relatives.

The same is true for those colleagues who are in a position of leadership or authority. When faced with the task of consoling a PTSD victim, they may feel that they should have the solutions to particular problems. They are used to formulating plans of action and are confused when faced with such a complex emotional condition. Simply visiting the victim can eventually be thought to be a futile exercise because it isn't actually *doing* anything.

It is at times of crisis that you find out exactly what your friendship and comradeship is worth. Some friends will stick by you, others will fade away into the background. Stick with those who stand by you. They are real friends who clearly value your company and want to help. They may not know how to help you, but cannot be criticized for trying. It is a tough time in any friendship.

Friends and colleagues can help by:

– being there,

75

– showing that they care,
– developing the skills of a good listener,
– trying to understand how trauma affects individuals,
– offering help with practical problems.

Of course, partners and family can also do all of the above, but because of their closeness to the victim they are involved in the care process more extensively and so will benefit from the 'break' that friends will be able to offer.

There are occasions when either family or friends are actively involved in the trauma itself. This can be an advantage, or a major problem. It is common in instances of sexual abuse for the guilty party to be a family member, maybe even a parent. This may result in the victim shutting-out the rest of the family until it can be established who can be trusted. In cases of sexual abuse, this is a serious dilemma for the victim, and such a situation can cause the break-up of the entire family if outside help is not quickly sought.

Family, friends or colleagues may have shared the traumatic experience with the PTSD victim. This shared experience may make it easier for those involved to discuss the event and work through the stresses of the situation in a type of group therapy. It may also have the opposite effect. 'We went through this together why has it not affected him the same way it affected me?' In this situation, feelings of guilt, failure, embarrassment and detachment may make discussion of the event virtually impossible.

Families can suffer if they are unable to approach the issues correctly. Families with trauma victims may be more inclined to outbursts of anger and violence. Their care skills and ability to be intimate may dwindle as poor communication leads to lack of trust and feelings of insecurity. A general dissatisfaction with life may become the predominant family mood. Victims are hard to cheer up, and can be prone to repeated recurrences of crisis and panic. Substance abuse and sexual dissatisfaction are problems which may occur.

There are some instances where the whole family has been traumatized by the event and so cannot help each other. Natural and man-made disasters have a habit of affecting entire families. The Aberfan and Buffalo Creek disasters, mentioned in the opening chapter, are prime examples.

Even the families with the very best coping strategies will need outside help at times like this.

Chapter five

Complications

Those who suffer from Post-Traumatic Stress Disorder have to negotiate an obstacle course in order to recover. It is necessary to examine in detail some of the hurdles that must be faced.

Complicating factors in PTSD are:

- Panic
- Depression
- Alcoholism
- Drug abuse
- Adverse publicity
- Ignorance of PTSD
- Relapses in recovery
- Physical and Sexual Abuse

PANIC

Attacks of panic can be extremely frightening, and totally exhausting. Recovery from a severe panic attack can take a considerable time – days rather than hours. So what happens when people say they are suffering from a panic attack?[1]

Following the traumatic event, certain sights, smells or sounds may spark off an instant warning that the event is about to be repeated. These 'triggers' are misinterpreted by the brain, and chemical messages within the body prepare you for a 'flight or fight' situation. If these triggers present themselves frequently, the brain repeats the messages and the body lunges from one panic to another.

The features of a panic attack vary from person to person, but some of the effects are common to most sufferers. The heart rate increases and breathing becomes more laboured. Some people start to pant, taking their breath in short, frequent gasps. Muscles, particularly in arms and legs, tighten and this causes considerable pain. In some instances people complain that their vision becomes clouded or blurred. Other people are convinced that they are going to faint. Occasionally, chest tightness and arm pains can become so intense that sufferers think they are having a heart attack. Such thoughts just add further fuel to the panic attack.

People in a state of panic are continually scanning their surroundings in a search for possible threats to their well-being. This is hypervigilance in the extreme.

In fact, collapsing or fainting is most unlikely. Panic alters the blood pressure in the opposite direction to that needed for fainting. The feelings of lightheadedness (which might also affect vision) arise simply because more oxygen is being pumped to the muscles (ready for fight or flight) and less is going to the brain.

Panic attacks can also cause worry and anxiety for those around you. They might think you are having some kind of fit, or a heart attack, and consequently, they might unintentionally make matters worse.

If you find yourself in a panic situation the easiest remedy is to remove yourself from the source of panic. Easy to say, but not always easy to achieve. Some people find themselves panicking whilst on public transport. However, if you are on your way home from work, are you going to get out and walk, or try to sit out the attack?

Paul:
Sitting in a coach, immediately behind the driver, I should have felt safe. I could see what was going on ahead. I knew every single person on the coach. We had all been on the same outing.

I felt the panic start. My fists clenched and my arms went as rigid as steel. I started to breathe more rapidly and I could feel my heart pounding inside my chest. I closed my eyes and tried to concentrate on my breathing. I had to fight off this panic.

It just got worse and worse. In the end they stopped the coach and I got out to walk around. I don't know what everyone thought about me. I looked like a drug addict suffering from withdrawal symptoms. I was shaking and sweating, and very unsteady on my feet.

The real problem was that I knew I had to get back on the coach to travel home. I felt so trapped and frightened. As I climbed back onto the coach I knew I was in for two hours of hell – but there was nothing I could do about it.

If you concentrate on your breathing and slow your breathing down, then the panic will start to lessen. A panic attack is a vicious cycle of stimuli and responses. What you have to try to do is break that circle of events by removing one or the other. By concentrating on your breathing pattern (response) and slowing your breathing down, it is possible to break the circle.

Breathe in slowly . . . counting as you do so . . . one, two, three, four, five. Then breathe out in much the same way . . . one, two, three, four, five, six. This technique makes you concentrate on the mechanics of breathing and distracts from the panic. It is helpful if someone with you can enforce the counting. If you are on your own you must try to do this yourself.

The other way of dealing with a panic attack is to remove the stimulus that caused the initial panic. This is sometimes easier and is a short-term solution, but it does mean that sooner or later you will have to face up to that stimulus once again.

David:
What happens when the phone rings? First, I panic. I get very hot and start to sweat. My breathing quickens and becomes less effective. My muscles tense up. If it is a particularly bad panic attack, my vision blurs, I become dizzy and I can actually hear my own pulse. It becomes impossible to pick up the telephone receiver. Rarely do I wonder who is calling.[2]

Panic attacks should not be taken lightly. Learn from your experiences and don't set tasks which are doomed to fail and distress you. Some people will advise that you can 'flood' yourself with the situation or object that causes panic. In that way, you will eventually overcome the fear and end the panic. This 'flooding' is an antiquated idea which was clearly devised by someone who had never suffered a panic attack. It could possibly be dangerous. It will certainly be exhausting and, if it fails, you might find yourself with an even greater fear of that stimulus. The flooding technique should be avoided by all PTSD sufferers.

Panic attacks are at their worst when they are triggered unexpectedly. As part of their treatment, many PTSD sufferers will be exposed to situations which cause panic attacks, but in a controlled way. Unfortunately, life is unpredictable and occasionally the circumstances which cause the panic will present themselves unexpectedly. The suddenness of this will intensify the panic attack, and it is this unplanned exposure to stimuli which often causes the most acute panic response. Because of this risk, PTSD victims tend to become very wary of new or untried situations.

Matthew:

I was a little on edge, but the train was almost empty. In my carriage there was just one other passenger. It was my first trip to London – my first trip to Europe since John's death.

Then, at Shepherd's Bush, a drunk got on and sat opposite me. He looked me up and down (posh suit and airline bag) and came out with the classic opener, 'What U . . . staring at?'

I looked away.

'You, c . . . , I asked you a question.'

I found a fascinating advert on the wall to examine in detail.

'Too posh to talk to me are you? Say something, even if it is . . . off.'

Tempting!

I looked at him.

'I don't really have anything to say.' I was amazed how calm my voice was. Inside I was panicking and just wanted to get out. Silly idea to use the tube anyway. The carriage suddenly felt full and very small.

Ladbroke Grove.

'You're . . . frightened of me, are you?'

'No.' I realized I was not at all frightened of him, but was

terrified of my surroundings.

'You make me . . . sick, you Yanks,' he stated bluntly. He stood and staggered towards me.

I stood up quickly.

I stepped to one side; his fist missed me. I then punched him really hard on the side of his mouth.

Paddington.

The doors opened and I charged out.

There are no short solutions to the treatment of panic attacks. Those sufferers who want to conquer their feelings of panic must have a finely-scheduled timetable of actions and tasks to grade their exposure to the situation that causes panic.

DEPRESSION

Only a person who has been so down that they have actually contemplated ending their life can truly understand such deep feelings of despair and depression. If you continually feel frightened, you cannot sleep, you cannot remember simple things and your poor concentration limits the number of things you can do, so it is only to be expected that gloomy feelings and despair will emerge. Many PTSD sufferers will experience periods of depression.

Jessica:
You feel isolated and very much alone – even in a crowded room. Life is no longer worth anything. There is no God, nobody cares and nothing has any purpose any more. It's frightening.

Depression, as a feature of PTSD, is a constellation of

different symptoms – a syndrome – so that not every depressed PTSD sufferer will have the same symptoms. Some of the most common symptoms of depression that are linked to PTSD are:

- Depressed mood most of the day, and nearly every day.
- Little interest or pleasure in any activity.
- Insomnia.
- Loss of energy nearly every day.
- Diminished ability to think clearly.
- Bouts of sadness, tearfulness or anger.
- Loss of interest in sex/food.
- Preoccupation with guilty feelings.
- Reduced concentration.
- Feelings of worthlessness/hopelessness.
- Recurrent thoughts of death/suicide.

If at least half of these symptoms can be applied to your present state of mind, then you are probably suffering from depression.

Overcoming these depressive feelings requires considerable effort, and help. Do not be afraid to seek help. Trying to cope with depression on your own can be dangerous. Help need not come from official medical sources such as family doctors or counsellors. Help can be gleaned from family and close friends. Firstly, YOU must acknowledge that you are feeling gloomy and that you want to do something to overcome those feelings. Admit the problem, there is no disgrace attached to it – you are not on trial. Then, you can start to seek out the solution.

If you feel that life has lost its flavour, then you must slowly start to re-establish things. Try to relax a little. Stop worrying about things over which you have no control. Concentrate on the things which you can change.

Question your reasons for feeling depressed:

- You might be feeling guilty. Are you being over-critical of yourself?
- You may consider that you are worthless. You are not.
- You may have a very low self-esteem. List your achievements.
- You may feel unloved. Look around at the people who care for you.

The list could go on. You must start to look at things in a positive way. When you look at a bottle of wine and notice that some of the contents have been drunk – say to yourself, 'This bottle is still half full.' Resist the thought that it is half empty. Think positively.

For those who are extremely depressed there is no substitute for professional advice and care. This might mean a course of therapy, or medication to see you through the crisis, because crisis is what it is. Resorting to medication is not a sign of failure. Refusing to acknowledge that you require outside help is the failing.

In some instances, depression is the first symptom of Post-Traumatic Stress Disorder to present itself. In these cases it is important to acknowledge that the trauma you have suffered previously may be linked to the very negative feelings that you are experiencing now. Before the depression can be effectively treated, the trauma will have to be explored through counselling. Dealing with the trauma in this way will often significantly ease the depression.

ALCOHOLISM

People with problems often resort to drinking. It happens in the movies all the time. 'What you need is a stiff drink!' There is nothing wrong with the occasional stiff drink. Alcohol does relax people, and being able to relax is very necessary. However, if the drinks are regular it will not be long before the *only* way you can relax is with a drink. Such a situation is the first step towards alcoholism.

> *Cindy:*
> *I started drinking when I was about 15. After the accident I got very fed up with everyone and started drinking even more. I would take bottles up to my room and drink the lot. It was costing me too much. That is when I realized exactly how much I was drinking.*

Alcohol is very handy for those people who cannot spontaneously disassociate themselves from events. It helps you to forget. It is no coincidence that the doctors portrayed in *M.A.S.H.,* the US TV series about the Korean War, built their own drinks still inside their tent. They drank in order to forget the war, to forget their loved ones back home (who they were missing) and to forget their misbehaving whilst they were away from their loved ones.

Using alcohol as a prop in this way can only have one outcome. You will become dependent upon it, just like any other drug addict. For a PTSD sufferer to have to break an addiction too, is asking a great deal. The addiction will have to be successfully treated before the PTSD can be treated, even though the PTSD may have been initially responsible for the alcoholism.

DRUG ABUSE

Much of what has been said about alcoholism is equally true of drug abuse. The main difference is that alcoholism is (within reason) legal and more socially acceptable in some circles. But both addictions can be fatal.

Perhaps there is an age differential here. Older PTSD sufferers may turn to drink, while younger sufferers may seek solace in drugs. Both groups are searching for a prop, something to help them through a difficult period in their lives. When people are desperate for help they will turn to anything or anyone who they think might be a source of comfort. Consequently, people who would never usually dream of using hard drugs, find themselves purchasing illegal substances.

ADVERSE PUBLICITY

We live in an age dominated by the mass media. Newspapers, television and radio companies make considerable sums of money by selling news. Any incident which involves personal grief or tragedy is actively followed by the public, via the media.

Clearly, anyone involved in a large-scale traumatic, potentially life-threatening, situation is going to become a focus for media attention. Even if the people involved manage to escape direct attention, the event itself is likely to attract news-hunters and they will suffer indirectly.

Graham:
The press got hold of the story, and turned it all around. They said I crashed the car, and then some youths threw stones at it. They tried to make out it was all my fault. I suppose it made a better story.

Even those of us who have never suffered a traumatic incident will have witnessed such events in our homes, thanks to television.

What were you doing on 22 November last year? What were you doing on the day President John F. Kennedy was assassinated (22 November 1963)? Over 30 years later, many people can recall incidents from that day because they were so emotionally struck by the murder that was screened around the world.

Because of this extensive, and almost instant, media coverage, people are brought to the scenes of major disasters whilst they are sitting in the security of their own homes. This security is invaded so suddenly that we can often find our living rooms transformed into a disaster scene without any opportunity to prepare ourselves for what we are about to experience.[3]

The pathetic sight of refugees and survivors; the devastation and destruction; the carnage. Film crews almost deliberately dwell on scenes that are going to tug on the emotions: a child's shoe; a toy; articles of clothing; a body. Such scenes can affect people who have no direct involvement other than watching a television screen in the privacy and comfort of their own homes.

Felicity:
It was November 1990, and I was watching some TV news film of Romanian orphans. The dark, wet, cold and smelly building they lived in was awful. I found tears running down my face. In a way, I felt as trapped as they were. They were victims, and I was a victim too. Seeing that piece of film made me realize I was trapped too. I cried a lot that night.

Sensationalizing the news can do much damage to some

survivors. It causes a deepening of the trauma, and often intrudes into private lives beyond the boundaries of acceptable behaviour.

The media have been instrumental in increasing public awareness of trauma. In consequence they have a great responsibility to bring news to the homes of millions, and to do this with a sympathetic and sensitive touch. What the media transmit influences the perceptions, attitudes and opinions of the world.

Publicity of any traumatic event usually has three stages to it. First, the event itself is covered in detail. The scale of the disaster will dictate how long this coverage might last. An air crash might be mentioned for just two or three news bulletins, and may appear in the newspapers in a couple of editions. A war, however, may totally dominate all media elements for months or years. This was the case during the Vietnam War and, more recently, the Persian Gulf War and the conflict in Bosnia.

Other occasions when the media choose to highlight a traumatic incident are usually confined to any legal cases which are brought as a result of the event.

Paul:
I was sitting at home watching the news. Suddenly I saw a picture of the boat on its side. Floodlights showed people waving their arms to the rescuers. I thought I was going to see myself at any moment. I couldn't look — but I couldn't look away either. I was sweating and shaking. My girlfriend thought I was going to have a fit or something, but I couldn't talk to her.

Four years after the incident, seeing those pictures made the whole thing real once again.

Paul had seen this piece of film before, several times. It was the standard archive clip that the BBC screened every time the incident was mentioned. What made it so difficult was the unexpectedness of the film. A small, and rather technical, legal issue was being debated and the film was intended to provide visual impact to the argument. The impact such a sudden screening had upon Paul was considerable. One moment he was sitting with his girlfriend in the safety of his own home. Then suddenly he was thrown emotionally backwards in time to the heart of the incident he was so busy trying to come to terms with. The sudden move from safety to danger resulted in the panic Paul felt.

This situation is common for any victim of a particularly newsworthy event. Time and time again, the same dramatic film clip will be produced to remind the rest of the audience what the traumatic event was like. Those who experienced the event first hand need no such reminders.

Anniversaries of events are often an excuse to show the same traumatic pictures again. Perhaps it is linked to the blessing of a memorial, or simply acting as a reminder to those unaffected by such tragedy. For the victims and the relatives of those who died, such anniversaries are painful occasions anyway. Even without visual reminders, those who are close to the event will be thinking about it on anniversaries. They may even seek out old press cuttings so as to check the accuracy of their own recollection of the event.

Marlene:
I opened up the scrap book and found the article from the local paper. They had an aerial photograph of the road junction, and

a horrible picture of me wearing my nursing uniform. I read
through the article, folded it back into the book and put it away
again. The reporter wrote that the accident was my friend's
fault. I have never believed that.

IGNORANCE OF PTSD

The whole world was ignorant of Post-Traumatic Stress
Disorder prior to 1980. In one or two instances, however,
communities were discovering that psychological trauma
was equally as debilitating as any physical injury. These
'invisible injuries' were slowly starting to attract interest in
the courts.

On both sides of the Atlantic, there were disasters which
led to communities suffering greatly. In Aberfan the
community was suffering grief brought about by the loss
of so many young lives. In Buffalo Creek the residents
were suffering similarly.

What helped increase the understanding of invisible
injuries was the decision by over 600 survivors of the
Buffalo Creek disaster to sue the Buffalo Mining
Company.[4] To do this they had to obtain evidence to show
that survivors of the incident suffered from psychological
injuries. Lawyers started to seek ways of proving the
existence of Post-Traumatic Stress Disorder.

During World War I there were army officers who
refused to believe there was such a illness as 'shell shock'.
In their view, these soldiers claiming to be suffering from
it were malingerers trying to find an excuse to be sent back
home. Following the war Europe suddenly contained
thousands of shell shock victims, and even the great
psychologist, Freud, acknowledged that these men were
suffering from a 'profound reaction to the conflict'.

By the Second World War, 'war-neurosis' was a well-established condition, and in 1939 it was agreed that this condition could prove very debilitating to soldiers. It was not considered to affect civilians, however.

Following the war in Vietnam the medical profession took the condition far more seriously, and by 1980 PTSD was well documented as an emotional condition. Unfortunately, after the war in the Persian Gulf there was a general reluctance by the governments of the European powers involved to admit that many, if any, combat veterans were suffering from PTSD. Statistics were available on most other aspects of the conflict, but not on the incidence of Post-Traumatic Stress.

Marlene:
In the army I met people who had served in Vietnam. You could be sitting and talking to them and suddenly you knew they were no longer listening. I used to think they were just bored. Now, I realize they were struggling to pay attention. Their mind was somewhere else. Their eyes were filled by images which were thousands of miles away.

Since my accidents I have thought about these veterans quite a bit. You see, I now have problems with attentiveness. I just switch off and my mind drifts on to other things. People must think I am so rude.

People who have been diagnosed as suffering from PTSD can often see symptoms of the disorder in others. However, most people think that being attentive is simply a matter of good manners. They cannot readily appreciate that there may be some medical reason why people appear to daydream. The ignorance about the problems faced by PTSD sufferers is overwhelming, and even extends to some doctors and healthcare workers.

David:
Before the police would let me retire I had to be examined by their medical officer. We sat and chatted for about 30 minutes and he concluded the medical by saying, 'I'm not sure about PTSD. You appear to have a sort of police phobia though.' Until that point, I thought he had understood me.

One of the most painful aspects of PTSD is the way that close family and friends react to the victim. Initially, there is plenty of support and understanding, but this becomes diluted by time. If, after several months, you are still showing signs of being unwell, you may find people becoming less sympathetic.

Richard:
During a police training exercise in which live petrol bombs were being thrown, an instructor thought it would be a good idea to set himself alight, then act as though he was being badly burned. I was not expecting this, and had only just returned to work after the fire. I ended up by knocking him to the ground and smothering the flames with an emergency fire extinguisher which was nearby.

I was reprimanded for using the extinguisher. I should first have tried to use other means to halt the blaze. Despite my protests nobody understood that I just couldn't bear to see someone on fire for a second longer than I had to. They told me to pull myself together!

Sometimes sufferers feel that nobody really understands what they are experiencing. This can be an extremely lonely sensation which can lead back to feelings of depression and anxiety.

If the original trauma is of a very private nature, these feelings of loneliness can become quite overwhelming. Victims of rape and sexual assaults don't usually tell many people about their trauma. In consequence, when they are seen to be behaving 'oddly' there are very few people who can understand why, and make allowances for this behaviour.

All of a sudden, a friendly pat on the shoulder, or a hug, can take on a different meaning to those who have become very wary of any physical contact or closeness. Within marriages and partnerships these victims may experience problems in coping with, and enjoying, intimacy. Great understanding of their plight is required. They have to learn to trust again.

To try and rush these relationships will do great harm. To suggest that your partner is cold, or malingering, or manipulating the relationship will inevitably lead to furious and vicious rows. It may even lead to hatred. Remember that most women who experience rape see it as a life-threatening event, having generally feared mutilation or death during the assault.[5] Reintroducing any sexual experience is necessarily a task requiring patience, gentleness, love and understanding.

Christine:
It was three days before I could tell my husband anything. During that time I managed to avoid sex altogether. Once I told him, he was angry with everyone and we still avoided each other. It was nearly two weeks before I could even cuddle him in bed. He said he understood. But in his eyes I could see that he was not always sure of things.

RELAPSES IN RECOVERY

With many types of illness there is a standard rate of recovery. A common cold lasts a week. Broken ribs require six weeks before they stop aching. Other, more serious ailments may take several months. With PTSD, however, there is no precise timescale and this can often cause concern to those who are suffering. 'When will I be better?' turns into 'Will I ever recover?'

PTSD is diagnosed when the victim of trauma has been suffering for more than one month. If the symptoms last for longer than six months then the condition has become chronic. Beyond that, there is no real yardstick. Every case is different.

PTSD sufferers find themselves playing a game of emotional snakes and ladders. The game board is the road to recovery, divided into one hundred squares, and is covered by a series of ladders which help you on the way up. Between the ladders are the snakes which may take you backwards toward the start of the game. However, on a true snakes and ladders board no snake can take you all the way back to square one. This analogy is probably more realistic than the very simplistic idea that recovery is a case of two steps forward and then one step back. Recovery is not that smooth, neither is it that predictable.

Many PTSD sufferers and their carers tend to set themselves goals or targets. Often these targets will be linked to the calender:

- 'I will return to work by 1 June.'
- 'I want to have stopped taking sleeping tablets by Christmas.'
- 'I intend to go out shopping on my own during my holiday.'

Formulating goals and targets is a very good strategy provided the targets are within reach. If the target is too difficult, then you are setting yourself up to fail. That serves no useful purpose.

Snakes and Ladders

A traditional snakes and ladders board has nine ladders to aid success and ten snakes to hinder your progress. The ladders are named after virtues such as 'Diligence' which stretches from square 28 up to 84 (reward). The snakes represent vices like 'Greed' which stretches from square 62 down to 19 (suffering).

FINISH 100	99	98	97	96	95	94	93	92	91
81	82	83	84	85	86	87	88	89	90
80	79	78	77	76	75	74	73	72	71
61	62	63	64	65	66	67	68	69	70
60	59	58	57	56	55	54	53	52	51
41	42	43	44	45	46	47	48	49	50
40	39	38	37	36	35	34	33	32	31
21	22	23	24	25	26	27	28	29	30
20	19	18	17	16	15	14	13	12	11
START 1	2	3	4	5	6	7	8	9	10

Set sensible, attainable, targets. Fix dates for accomplishing tasks which are a reasonable time away. If you reach the target before the date, then treat yourself – you have done well. Far better to do this, than to set an almost impossible task and fail miserably.

Inevitably, some targets are not going to be achieved. Life is full of unpredictable events and something will always happen that is likely to knock you off course. That's life! Allow for the unexpected in your preparation of targets. Give yourself a breathing space in your planning. Targets are wonderful when they are achieved, but terrible if you are defeated by them. Do not set yourself up to fail. Do not try to rush your recovery by setting dates which you cannot reasonably be expected to reach.

Remember the snakes and ladders board. If you do fail to reach a target, that failure does not drag you all the way back to square one. Even in failing, you have learned something about how best to set the next target.

PHYSICAL AND SEXUAL ABUSE

The link between PTSD and both physical and sexual abuse is the subject of other texts.[6] However, the subjects are often so closely linked that it is unwise to discuss one without at least mentioning the other.

Some sufferers are PTSD victims as a direct result of abuse. This may be physical abuse or domestic battering. It may be sexual abuse such as rape or incest. There are also a number of people who have suffered traumatic, potentially life-threatening events, and who have a previous history of either physical or sexual abuse. There are studies which suggest that people who have previously been abused in some way are more likely to suffer from

PTSD following a traumatic event. That does not mean that every PTSD victim has been the subject of such abuse, but some have.

Sexual abuse has no discrimination, it can occur to anyone. People of all ages, all social classes, all ethnic groups and both sexes have suffered from this kind of abuse. However, rape and sexual abuse are the only violent crimes in which women are more likely to be victims than men.

Examples of abuse leading to PTSD

Wife battering	Husband battering	Child battering
Date rape	Gang rape	Rape in marriage
Incest	Prostitution	Child rape

Abuse of any kind may affect victims in a variety of ways. Clearly, their health will suffer. There may be physical injuries inflicted; there are almost certainly psychological (invisible) injuries sustained. There is also the possibility of pregnancy for females, and of contracting sexually transmitted diseases for both sexes. Many abuse victims will experience the intrusive and physical symptoms of PTSD and will seek to become avoidant in their actions.

The victims will experience a whole range of feelings and emotions and may be unable to control their emotional swings. They may alternate between anger and fear; helplessness and vulnerability; sadness and depression; guilt and shame. They will experience feelings of being responsible for what has happened to them. Such an emotional turmoil is extremely confusing and difficult to control.

Some victims may experience a phenomenon known as

the 'Stockholm syndrome'[7]. During a bank robbery in Stockholm in 1973 some people were held hostage by the robbers. During the traumatic incident the hostages developed feelings of admiration, sympathy and empathy with their captors. In turn, the captors developed a degree of sympathy and admiration for their hostages. This has since been repeated in other hostage situations and also has similarities with the relationship between the 'abused' and their 'abuser'.

It is possible that these feelings of sympathy are responsible for the ties of loyalty in cases of abuse and battering. It may be the main reason for some abuse situations becoming so prolonged. There is often a reluctance by the victim to expose the culprit for exactly what he or she is: a person who enjoys malicious acts which cause hurt and pain to others.

Prolonged abuse can have a devastating effect upon the lives of the victims. Basic daily activities and relationships can suffer. Formal education will be adversely affected in younger abuse victims. Adult abuse victims may struggle to maintain a satisfactory partnership, be poor parents, wrestle with their career and play a lesser part in community life than they would originally have wished. Many victims allow the feelings of guilt and shame to dominate their lives.

PROLONGED TRAUMATIC STRESS

The betrayal of trust is a particular concern of the victims of prolonged abuse. Some psychologists have labelled these victims as suffering from PDSD (Prolonged Duress Stress Disorder) as opposed to PTSD. The symptoms and treatment of the two disorders are almost identical, but the reason for the suffering is a series of distressing events rather than just one very traumatic event. In the case of emergency service personnel it is sometimes difficult to ascertain whether they are suffering from PTSD following one very traumatic event, or PDSD as a result of dealing with a whole series of distressing incidents. This accumulation of stressful incidents produces a PTSD-like response in the sufferer, but cannot officially be described as Post-Traumatic Stress Disorder. PDSD is sometimes referred to as 'Rolling PTSD' within the emergency services where prolonged traumatic stress is a fact of life.[8]

People who have been abused at the hands of others have difficulty in trusting again. Trust is especially important if you intend to discuss a traumatic event. When victims decide to disclose what has happened to them they have selected that person because they truly trust them. If that trust is betrayed, they will not be so ready to trust another person.

When looking for a person to trust, look for two attributes. Look for someone whose behaviour is predictable, and who has broadly similar values to your own.

The predictable behaviour is necessary because when a trusted confidant says he will do something, or be somewhere at a specific time, you expect him to do that. If you are let down repeatedly by the person's unpredictable behaviour, then you are unlikely to be able to trust that person fully.

The second element of trust is having similar values. Are you in general agreement on the basic values of life? Do you both have the same degree of respect for other people? Do you both treat confidential information in the same way? Can you trust this person and tell them everything?

These are the questions in the mind of every person seeking counsel, but are even more dominant in the mind of an abused or battered person who may have been exploited as a result of trusting someone close to them on previous occasions: their abuser.

Chapter six

People who can help

It is unlikely that anyone can make a full recovery from Post-Traumatic Stress Disorder on their own. They will require help from various sources. The longer they try to cope without help, the longer the condition is likely to persist.

PTSD is a state of mind. It is not possible for the victims to control the symptoms until they are explained in a rational and acceptable fashion. The term 'mental illness' conjures up all manner of unpleasant images for many people, but it is often the term linked to PTSD. Because of this, I prefer to call PTSD an emotional condition.[1] However, this labelling is something which the victim has to come to terms with – and this is not easy within a society that is generally afraid of the label 'mentally ill'.

Help for PTSD sufferers comes in many guises and from a variety of different occupations.

Family doctors

Hospitals and
   convalescent homes

Chiropractors

Counsellors

Independent help groups

Psychologists

Psychiatrists

Physiotherapists

Complementary health
   practitioners

Religious groups

WHEN DO YOU NEED HELP?

PTSD cannot be formally diagnosed until one month has gone by since the episode which triggered off the disorder. However, immediately after the trauma, victims may experience very disturbing symptoms and that is a very normal reaction. In fact, if the symptoms of post-trauma stress are treated as they occur, the likelihood of developing Post-Traumatic Stress Disorder is reduced.

There are nine situations which should indicate to you that it is time to seek help for PTSD:[2]

1 If you feel you cannot handle intense feelings or body sensations. If you feel that your emotions are not falling into place over a period of time. If you feel chronic tension, confusion, emptiness or exhaustion.
2 If you continue to have nightmares and a poor pattern of sleep.
3 If after a month you continue to feel numb and empty. If you have to keep active in order not to feel this way.
4 If you have no person or group with whom to share your emotions and you feel the need to do so.
5 If your relationships seem to suffer badly, or if sexual problems develop.
6 If you have accidents through lack of concentration.
7 If you smoke, drink or take drugs to excess since the event.
8 If your work performance suffers.
9 If, as a helper, you are suffering from 'exhaustion'.

The month after a traumatic event is a period when you must be extra careful in everything you do. It is a time when you are at greater risk of having a road accident because you are in an upset state and probably less able to concentrate on what you are doing. It is also a time when accidents in the home are more likely to occur. Take extra care in the kitchen when preparing food, and take care when using any household appliances. With household chores, do not take any shortcuts which could prove dangerous.

Probably the first person who discusses the issue of help with you is a close relative, friend or colleague. It may be that you ask for their advice on the matter. Should you seek help? If you are asking the advice of friends, then why not go that one step further and seek the advice of a professional? In many instances, the first person you turn to is your own family doctor. This is a logical step and I have no doubt you will be given a sympathetic hearing. Do not make light of your troubles. If they are serious enough for you to be considering discussing them with a professional, then they are serious enough for him or her to take notice.

Probably the first task you will be asked to do is to complete some form of questionnaire to establish the scale of the event you experienced. There are many standard tests used to assess this. Some have been adapted and tailored to suit specific events which have effected many people. Others are of a standard type that could be applied to a variety of situations. They are nothing to be frightened of. The tests are simply a method of gauging a person's emotional state at any particular time. Some practitioners like to give these tests to their patients at regular intervals to measure any progress which may have taken place.

There are many types and styles of test. None should

prove difficult and it is not a question of passing or failing. By asking a series of basic questions and grading your reply the test is simply a tool to assist with the best possible diagnosis of your condition. Some questionnaires take a different form. They may appear as a simple check list, or as an assessment of your mood. All test results, like any other part of your treatment, will be treated in the strictest confidence.

Work and Social Adjustment Screening Test

People's problems sometimes affect their ability to do certain things in their day-to-day lives. How do your problems affect your ability to: (please circle one number):

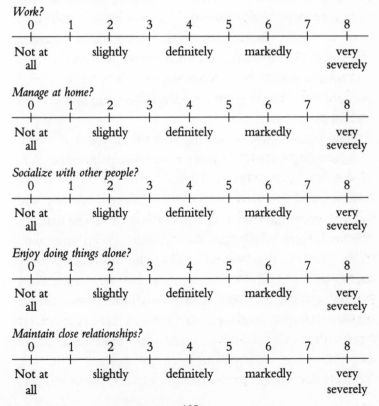

Work?

0	1	2	3	4	5	6	7	8
Not at all		slightly		definitely		markedly		very severely

Manage at home?

0	1	2	3	4	5	6	7	8
Not at all		slightly		definitely		markedly		very severely

Socialize with other people?

0	1	2	3	4	5	6	7	8
Not at all		slightly		definitely		markedly		very severely

Enjoy doing things alone?

0	1	2	3	4	5	6	7	8
Not at all		slightly		definitely		markedly		very severely

Maintain close relationships?

0	1	2	3	4	5	6	7	8
Not at all		slightly		definitely		markedly		very severely

The most common type of test is the Beck Inventory or the Impact of Events test. Others may include a Fear Questionnaire, a work and social adjustment screening checklist, or a general health checklist.

The work and social screening test (see example) is simply a way of establishing what is bothering you – it is your view of what is wrong at the present time. By working through the five headings, you gauge your ability to cope with particular things. For question one, if you are coping quite well at work then you might award yourself a score of perhaps *one*. If work is intolerable then you might score *seven* or even *eight*.

Work through the rest of the questions and be honest with yourself. If your total score is 16 or more then you could definitely benefit from some form of treatment. If your score is over 29 then it is vitally important that you seek treatment soon. Delaying treatment only makes things worse.

Do this test again after a few weeks of treatment. Your score *will* be lower: perhaps only a few points lower, but definitely an improvement.

The next questionnaire (see examples) requires you to think about your condition over the past week. The questionnaire is a list of 12 statements made by PTSD sufferers and you are asked to highlight the frequency with which these comments are true for you. You will see from the two examples that the answers given are quite different. The two respondents who completed these examples both suffered with chronic Post-Traumatic Stress Disorder. Tests such as the Impact of Life Events require expert interpretation. However, by repeating the test yourself over a period of time, the answering crosses should move slowly and steadily towards the left. Remember the snakes and ladders board!

People who can help

IMPACT OF LIFE EVENTS QUESTIONNAIRE

Date: 24 Jan 1988

NAME   PAUL

ON   6 March 1987   YOU EXPERIENCED   a ship sinking

Below is a list of comments made by people after stressful life events. Please check each item, indicating how frequently these comments were true for you DURING THE PAST SEVEN DAYS. If they did not occur during that time, please mark the 'not at all' column.

	FREQUENCY			
	Not at all	Rarely	Sometimes	Often
I thought about it when I didn't mean to.			✓	
I tried to remove it from my mind.				✓
I had waves of strong feeling about it.		✓		
I had dreams about it.				✓
I stayed away from reminders about it.		✓		
I tried not to talk about it.		✓		
Pictures about it popped into my mind.				✓
Other things kept making me think about it.		✓		
I tried not to think about it.				✓
Any reminders brought back feelings about it.			✓	
My feelings about it were kind of numb.	✓			
Thoughts about it prevented me from sleeping.				✓

107

IMPACT OF LIFE EVENTS QUESTIONNAIRE

Date: 6 Jan 1992

NAME   CHRISTINE

ON   3 September 1991   YOU EXPERIENCED   rape

Below is a list of comments made by people after stressful life events. Please check each item, indicating how frequently these comments were true for you DURING THE PAST SEVEN DAYS. If they did not occur during that time, please mark the 'not at all' column.

	FREQUENCY			
	Not at all	Rarely	Sometimes	Often
I thought about it when I didn't mean to.				✓
I tried to remove it from my mind.			✓	
I had waves of strong feeling about it.			✓	
I had dreams about it.				✓
I stayed away from reminders about it.			✓	
I tried not to talk about it.	✓			
Pictures about it popped into my mind.				✓
Other things kept making me think about it.		✓		
I tried not to think about it.			✓	
Any reminders brought back feelings about it.			✓	
My feelings about it were kind of numb.		✓		
Thoughts about it prevented me from sleeping.				✓

All tests rely heavily upon the honesty of the candidate. If you make attempts to cheat in such tests you will only be cheating yourself. You have nothing to gain and everything to lose by entering false answers.

The tests are also reliant upon correct interpretation of the results. Tests in a book are all very well and will prepare you for the type of experience you have to face, but they can be no substitute for the real thing. Remember, these tests are nothing to fear.

Many family doctors will be unfamiliar with Post-Traumatic Stress Disorder. They may have only seen a handful of cases and be unsure what treatment to offer. Consequently they will wish to refer your case to somebody with more expertise in the field. This is no criticism of family doctors. They follow similar procedures when they deal with many other ailments. Accept such a referral in good faith.

Some trauma victims are first admitted to hospital. Victims of large-scale events can be processed in what appears to be an impersonal manner. Some hospitals operate a system of numbering casualties and constantly referring to them by that number. This is not a deliberate attempt to distress and dehumanize victims – it simply makes the quick processing of large numbers of casualties easier to administer.

Early symptoms of Post-Traumatic Stress can show very soon after the incident. Some symptoms may be present whilst the victim is still in the Accident and Emergency Department of the hospital. In some instances the symptoms may manifest themselves when the victim is transferred to a ward.

David:

The crowd closed in on me. I could just see a sea of faces. I hit out hard, and tried to move away. Hands grabbed at my arms and somebody sat across my legs. Then I could hear somebody calling my name.

I felt a little dizzy as I looked about me and realized I was surrounded by nursing staff. I was fighting with the nursing staff!

The hospital should be prepared for such reactions if they know they are dealing with the victims of trauma. The trouble is, the hospital staff may not know you have suffered a serious, potentially life-threatening event.

Richard:

A colleague came into the hospital to take my statement. He kept on and on about the guy who had started the fire. He went into great detail about how the fire had started and how badly injured the rest of the family were.

I was shaking badly and spent most of the time jumping whenever a door closed or somebody dropped something. I couldn't concentrate on the statement. I didn't want to talk about the fire.

Occasionally, the slightest little thing can be a trigger which sets off a series of events in the mind of the victim.

Cindy:

They kept me in hospital overnight because I had been knocked out. They said I was suffering from concussion. My head was still ringing from the blow I had received from the ladder. I was tucked up in bed, and they settled me down for the night.

I eventually fell asleep.

There was a loud metallic crash. Somebody dropped something near my bed. Instantly, I was awake and I could picture the building site. I could hear the sounds of men at work and I wanted to get away from it all. I jumped out of bed and ran. I was convinced I was in danger if I remained where I was. I tried to 'hide' in a corner of the corridor. It must have looked really funny. Two nurses came after me and stopped a few yards from where I crouched.

Nobody said anything. The nurses just didn't know what had happened to me. I stood up, slowly. I was in hospital, not by the building site. I could feel the tears. Why had I run away like that? What was wrong with me?

It is quite normal to be disorientated following a traumatic event. The body is in shock and the chemical messages being triggered by the brain are causing internal confusion amongst the senses. It might feel strange, or frightening. Victims might think they are acting abnormally and that they are out of control. This is not the case.

During the traumatic event, the protective mechanisms of the body were overloaded, passing messages and trying to predict dangers. As you were experiencing an abnormal situation the body did not know what to expect and so tried to prepare for everything. Having set your body this totally impossible task it should be of no surprise that it is going to take time for your body chemistry to re-adjust to the safety in which you now find yourself. This is normal.

Hospital staff should be aware of this and act accordingly. You should be given time to talk and explain why you are so distressed. Explain why you thought you were in danger. What did you think was going to happen to you?

In one respect, those who experience a large-scale traumatic event have an advantage. They will be amongst other victims who experienced the same event, and those who are caring for them will anticipate some of the symptoms of Post-Trauma Stress. Those people who experience more isolated traumatic incidents do not have this dubious advantage. Their carers will have no idea that they have suffered a serious and potentially life-threatening event.

Felicity.

My friend's parents suggested that I go and see my doctor. I couldn't really understand why! I was not ill or sick, so why see a doctor?

In the end I did go. The doctor was great. She simply sat and listened to my story. She did not examine me. There were no difficult questions. At the end of my appointment she did not even give me a prescription. It was not like any other doctor's appointment I have had. Yet I felt so much better afterwards.

Attending hospital or seeing your family doctor are usually the first steps towards obtaining help and relief from the symptoms of Post-Traumatic Stress Disorder. This is the starting point for most sufferers.

Thereafter, there are numerous courses of treatment open to sufferers. Don't be dismissive of anything you are offered. Keep an open mind on most treatments and assess the merits of each one. Treatments can be divided into two groups:

1 Those that treat the intrusive and avoidant symptoms.
2 Those that treat the physical symptoms of PTSD.

Psychiatrists, psychologists, counsellors, religious groups and self-help groups tend to concentrate on treating the intrusive and avoidant symptoms, while physiotherapists, chiropractors and natural health practitioners deal with the physical symptoms of the condition. It is usually the job of the family doctor to liaise and mediate between all these specialists and to have an overview of your treatment. Everything should be reported back to your doctor so that he may co-ordinate your recovery.

Reminder of the symptoms of PTSD

INTRUSIVE
- Recurrent and distressing recollections; flashbacks, thoughts, nightmares, dreams.
- Phobias about specific daily routines, events or objects.
- Feelings of guilt for having survived.

AVOIDANT
- Detachment from others, emotional numbness.
- Avoidance of thoughts or feelings associated with the event.
- Markedly diminished interest or pleasure in most activities.

PHYSICAL
- Sleep problems.
- Irrational or impulsive behaviour.
- Increased irritability.
- Impaired memory.
- Inability to concentrate.
- Hyperviligance.
- Exaggerated startle response.

- Violent outbursts.
- Joint/muscle pains.
- Feelings of nervousness.

CO-EXISTENT – Depression/anxiety.

Clearly by treating some intrusive symptoms the effect of physical symptoms will also be lessened. Indeed, treating any symptom will help overall. The simplest way to look at the methods of treatment is to examine them according to what they set out to achieve.

TREATMENT OF INTRUSIVE AND AVOIDANT SYMPTOMS

Recent studies of the role of neurotransmitters in the victim's brain have resulted in exciting advances in modern medicine. There is probably a simple chemical explanation for Post-Traumatic Stress Disorder, but at the present time this can only be guessed at. What is certain, is that the chemical messages transmitted by the brain during times of crisis can be overstretched in some way. The messages have become confused and there are too many of them. To treat the intrusive and avoidant symptoms of PTSD is to rectify and steady the flow of these chemical messages.

The chemical messengers which are of particular importance are the neurotransmitters known as noradrenaline and adrenaline, (called norepinephrine and epinephrine in America), endorphins and serotonin. The noradrenaline alerts the brain to the crisis. The endorphins help to calm us down and deal with the crisis while at the same time act as a pain killer. During severe stress, serotonin is depleted and the reason for this is unclear. It is believed that the decrease of these neurotransmitters following a traumatic event leads a traumatized person to feel depressed. The depression experienced by victims of PTSD is chemically different from depression in non-traumatized persons.

Many PTSD symptoms are brought about by faulty chemical messages being transmitted within the body. Prescribed drugs can be administered to rectify these chemical imbalances but this is a short-term treatment. The long-term solution is to 'talk it out', and become so at ease with discussing the trauma that the chemical messages of panic are no longer triggered. This is a job for an expert. Trauma counsellors, psychiatrists and psychologists are all trained to help victims control these triggers. It is often a slow process but it is the long-term treatment to cure PTSD.

TREATMENT OF PHYSICAL SYMPTOMS

The aches and pains linked to any stress can be severe. Those linked to PTSD can be simply awful. Limbs can be so tense that the pain in muscles becomes unbearable. Backache and headaches can also dominate daily existence.

Sleeplessness, irritability, poor memory, outbursts of violence and other physical symptoms can all be linked to the way we feel. There are several ways of relieving these symptoms. Some involve conventional treatments while others resort to natural remedies. All of them have been found to help ease the situation.

To be able to take full advantage of any counselling you must be able to relax. When your body is very tense, relaxing becomes almost impossible. Well-meaning people telling you to relax just makes matters worse. Your body will need help to relax it and that help can take a variety of forms.

Physiotherapy is most often linked to aiding recovery from physical injuries. To attend a physiotherapist with an 'invisible' or psychological injury may appear rather odd. Indeed, a few physiotherapists may turn you away. Fortunately most will admit you to their clinic and, as soon as they feel how tense your body has become, they will appreciate your need for treatment.

The same can be said for chiropractors. The tensions and aches caused by PTSD can be soothed and eased considerably by the attentions of a qualified chiropractor.

There are a variety of natural health practitioners who can help victims re-learn how to relax. Best known are aromatherapists and practitioners of reflexology, and other massage techniques such as shiatsu.

It is one of the paradoxes of the 1990s that in this high-tech age the wonderful healing properties of essential oils, herbs, massage and simple relaxation techniques are being reintroduced to the complex world of health-care.

It would be difficult to describe every treatment for PTSD in one book. However, it is necessary to explain a variety of different treatments and to show how they have been found to work effectively. Each victim will respond differently to treatment. Some treatments will be found wanting in some instances. Don't let the failure of one course of treatment discourage you from trying something different. Remember the snakes and ladders board.

Whatever treatments you choose to follow, remember the importance of having one person overseeing your total treatment. With such an arsenal of weaponry available to combat the symptoms of PTSD it is necessary to have one person to marshal these treatments into some logical progression. Counselling must be combined with relaxation techniques. Medication may be required at various stages of your recovery to help overcome the feelings of depression, frustration and anxiety. The one person best placed to oversee all of these treatments is your family doctor.

The next chapter examines some methods of treatment which have been found to succeed in the 10 cases which are highlighted in this book.

Chapter seven

Treatments

DRUG THERAPY

There are a number of drugs that can help PTSD victims on the road to recovery. The list includes:

1 Antidepressants
   (a) tricyclic antidepressants (TCAs)
   (b) monoamine oxidase inhibitors (MAOIs)
   (c) serotonin uptake inhibitors
2 Hypnotics (sleeping tablets)
3 Beta-adrenoceptor blockers (beta-blockers)
4 Analgesics (pain killers)

In many cases of Post-Traumatic Stress the chemical balance within the body has been badly disturbed. These prescribed drugs help that balance return to normal.

Look upon medication as a way of getting your course of treatment started. Following a traumatic, potentially life-threatening event the body is in chaos. It takes some time for the brain to accept that the danger has passed. Physically, your body is exhausted and needs a rest. The medication is a good way of resting the body so that it is fit to make a recovery from the trauma.

Medication can help reduce pain and shaking, ease

sleeping and aid relaxation. Tablets will not do the whole job for you, but they will help considerably by reducing anxiety levels.

However, if you are anxious about taking the medication this is counter-productive. Discuss the possible options with your doctor. Be guided by him, but make the final decision yourself. Discuss the possible side-effects of taking some of these drugs. Find out how long you are likely to be needing the drug. The length of some courses of treatment may seem daunting to some sufferers, but some of these drugs do not even begin to work effectively until they have been taken regularly for several weeks.

It is worthwhile taking a brief look at each of the four main groups of drugs on offer to PTSD sufferers.

1. Antidepressants

These drugs are not only administered to people who have a classic case of depression. Depression often exists alongside PTSD and it is right that that depression should be treated. Using antidepressant drugs is one way of treating depression in traumatized people. Antidepressants can also be used to treat loss of appetite, sleep disturbances and panic disorders.

There are several groups of antidepressant drug. Most common are the tricyclic drugs which are the original antidepressants and include *amitriptyline* and *imipramine*. Should these prove unsuccessful patients may be prescribed monoamine oxidase inhibitors (MAOIs) such as *phenelzine* and *isocarboxazid*. However, patients taking MAOI antidepressants have to maintain very strict control of their diet. They cannot eat cheese, pickled herring or broad bean pods. Neither should they drink any meat or yeast extract beverages like Bovril, Vegemite, Oxo or Marmite.

There are other drugs which have antidepressant properties, and the one which PTSD victims are most likely to be prescribed is a drug which inhibits the update of serotonin in the body, called *fluoxetine hydrochloride.*

Alcohol should be avoided by all patients taking antidepressants. The drugs exaggerate the effect of alcohol on the brain. They may make you drunk very quickly.

Many drugs have side-effects and antidepressants are no exception to this. A good doctor will explain the possible side-effects which might be experienced. There is no way of predicting which patients will be adversely affected by which drugs. Most antidepressants must be taken, as prescribed, for at least three weeks before any benefits of the drug can be appreciated.

Christine:
I couldn't sleep. I couldn't eat. I didn't want to do anything. I was sick inside. Eventually, I agreed to take some pills but I just took one or two and they didn't seem to work. Then my doctor gave me a good talking to. He explained that there was no magical overnight cure. It wasn't a case of take one of these and it will cheer you up. I then started to take the pills properly. After about four weeks I felt considerably better. I suffered from a dry mouth and so drank lots of fruit juice but that was much better than feeling so depressed.

Views on the quantity of the drug prescribed vary significantly. In the case of *amitriptyline* many psychiatrists recommend 125mg or 150mg daily as being a good therapeutic dose. However, many patients cannot tolerate more than 85mg without the quality of their life being adversely affected. Dose levels can be easily adjusted to suit individual needs.

David:

At first I was given one antidepressant for a few weeks. The side-effects were awful. I felt drunk and couldn't wake up properly. I had a headache nearly all the time.

So I was changed to another drug. That worked well for a couple of months but then I began to experience side-effects from that drug too.

Finally, after several other failures, I was given fluoxetine hydrochloride. Almost no side-effects after four months taking it.

Withdrawal from antidepressants should be gradual. In many cases complete withdrawal takes one or two months.

2. Hypnotics

Sleep is a problem for many PTSD sufferers. In the short term it is sometimes necessary to prescribe drugs which help regulate a pattern of sleep. Such drugs are usually prescribed over a short period of time at stages in recovery where victims are near exhaustion due to lack of sleep.

Paul:

I just needed something to help me sleep. I would lie awake for hours worrying about all kinds of things. Then, when I did get off to sleep I would wake up at about three o'clock in the morning and that would be the end of the night as far as I was concerned.

My doctor gave me some sleeping tablets, just enough to last me for two weeks. That saw me over a bad patch and although I didn't sleep for very long when I came off the drugs, my quality of sleep had improved.

Drugs such as *loprazolam* and *temazepam* act for a short time and they have little or no hang-over effect the following morning. There are some problems with withdrawal from these hypnotics in a few cases.

3. Beta-adrenoceptor blockers

Beta-blockers do work well for some PTSD victims. They reduce symptoms such as palpitations, sweating and shaking and so reduce the worry and fear that these symptoms produce.

Although they were not originally intended for this treatment, beta-blockers relieve the symptoms of hypertension and anxiety and are very useful in reducing the effects of panic experienced by some PTSD sufferers.

4. Analgesics

Many PTSD victims suffer with pain brought about by physical injuries and other pains brought on by tension, stress and cramp. On occasions these pains can become severe. Preparations such as aspirin, paracetamol and codeine can be purchased without prescription and many PTSD sufferers administer their own analgesics to relieve pain. However, on some occasions the pain may be so strong that a prescribed medication is required.

In any event, sufferers who are already taking drugs prescribed by their doctor should check with their doctor or pharmacist before self-administering any pain-killers. Not all drugs mix with one another and it is as well to check first.

When dealing with any drug which affects the central nervous system care should be taken, and professional advice sought.

Some of the unwanted side-effects of medication

Physical

Nausea	Headache	Vomiting
Blurred vision	Constipation	Tinnitus
Diarrhoea	Dizziness	Vertigo
Rashes	Low blood pressure	Lethargy
Impotence	Loss of libido	Numbness

Psychological

Anxiety	Poor concentration	Confusion
Agoraphobia	Panic attacks	Irritability
Tension	Emotional numbness	Obsessions
Social withdrawal	Depression	Poor memory
Aggressive outbursts		Disinhibition

It can be seen from the above table that some of the side-effects of certain drugs are the same as the symptoms of PTSD. Consequently, these side-effects become difficult to recognize for what they are.[1] It should be stressed that whilst some people never experience any side-effects, the chances of them occurring increase with long-term use.

PSYCHOTHERAPY

Some people avoid the term 'psychotherapy'. It simply means the treatment of nervous disorders by psychological methods. This type of therapy is practised by psychiatrists, psychologists and the counsellors employed by various help groups. Psychotherapy can help to reduce the effect of the intrusive and avoidant symptoms experienced by PTSD sufferers.

Within the field of psychotherapy there exists a large variety of different approaches to the treatment of PTSD. It is impractical to explain them all, but the most common forms of therapy are counselling, real life exposure and imaginal exposure.

Counselling involves sitting down and talking to someone – someone who you can trust totally. This may be a close friend or relative, or it may be a professional counsellor working within the health service or for a voluntary group or organization. Some employers also provide counsellors to care for the psychological needs of their workforce.

Victims of trauma often have a very negative view of things. Those who go on to develop PTSD will regularly have a low expectation of life and will often become depressed as a result. The job of a counsellor is not to change the negative thoughts and feelings into positive ones, but to turn them into *realistic* ones.

A textbook counselling session will be divided into three parts. The digging into the trauma, or 'dirty work', will be done during the first third of the session. Any exploration of that 'digging' will be carried out during the middle session, leaving the final third of the counselling session to settle and calm the client. That is the 'rule of thirds' theory.[2]

With PTSD sufferers the drop-out rate from counselling sessions is high: higher than the drop-out rate for clients suffering with depression or anxiety. This being the case, counsellors are under pressure to relax PTSD victims and not to alienate them. Exactly how this is achieved is up to the individual counsellor.

Consequently a typical PTSD counselling session might

start by enquiring into the sufferer's current state; a look at the high points and low points in the last few days. This might be followed up by a review of the previous session's homework. (Yes! Counsellors give homework assignments!) The session may then move into a period of 'dirty work'. This may well lead into the setting of more homework and conclude with any feedback on the day's session.

This example does not strictly follow the 'rule of thirds', but in the real world of counselling it is not always possible to stick with theoretical models.

Any counsellor worthy of the title will be totally loyal and treat anything discussed during the session in the strictest confidence. It may take several meetings before a good client-counsellor link can be established. That is not unusual. For those sufferers who come from a macho background it will be hard to be totally honest about emotions and feelings. However, total honesty is what is required if the sessions are to have any real benefit.

Clearly the first few meetings with your counsellor will be largely devoted to a description of the traumatic event which led you to feel that your life was under threat. For the sufferers who experienced one single incident this can be a straightforward narrative. For those who have suffered a repeated trauma, it is not practical to describe each incident as a separate issue. There may be too many and the memories of similar events will have blurred together. Usually, however, there are a few distinct and meaningful incidents which have remained freshest in the memory.

Some PTSD sufferers will be unsure what has caused the disorder to manifest itself. They will be taken through various stages in their life by the counsellor in order to find the real trauma which has affected them so deeply.

Being counselled can be both distressing and exhausting. A one-hour counselling session can totally sap the physical strength of the strongest person. If this is happening the counsellor will sense this and slow down the rate at which counselling tasks are set for you. Using the snakes and ladders board image, it is worth reminding yourself that you may have to slide down one or two snakes before you find the correct route to the winning square at the top of the board.

> *Graham:*
> *My wife is of the opinion that the PTSD was brought on by the counsellors at the convalescent home. I felt well and showed no sign of PTSD before attending them. Could the sessions have triggered it off?*

It is most unlikely that a counsellor will induce PTSD in a client. However, a counsellor may bring the condition to the surface and expose feelings which have been submerged for some time. It may well feel that the counselling has made you worse instead of better. That belief will only be short-lived.

> *Jessica:*
> *I couldn't work out what had happened to me. I used to be so happy-go-lucky but after the baby I started to worry so much. It was not until after she started school that I saw a counsellor and the subject of Post-Traumatic Stress was mentioned. I took a bit of convincing at first, but eventually I became so relieved to find that what I was experiencing was 'normal'. My counsellor helped me to see this. He was very patient with me.*

Sometimes we are frightened that people are going to

laugh, or suggest that the trauma was caused by our own mismanagement of the situation. These thoughts can be a barrier to successful counselling and will have to be addressed at some point, sooner rather than later.

Felicity:
My probation officer suggested that I should see a counsellor. Eventually I agreed. When I first saw her I talked about drug taking and boys. I talked about my fear of the police and of my father's drinking and driving conviction. I made out that I had been around and knew a thing or two. Eventually all this silly talk dried up and I was quieter. Then one day I walked into a session and told her about my brother and what he had done. She did not show any shock. She did not say I was a worthless slut, or anything like that.

I realized that I trusted my counsellor. It was such a relief to me.

Good counselling is non-judgemental. Counsellors are not there to give moral lectures or to say that things could have been better if you had done this, or done that. Counsellors will help you look at the trauma head-on and realize that you have coped remarkably well with this potentially life-threatening event. You are normal.

Counsellors often give their clients homework. Realistically, PTSD sufferers cannot hope to find a solution to their troubles during a weekly one-hour counselling session. There has to be more than that. Sufferers may be asked to keep a diary: writing briefly about what has happened, how they feel, what they are worried about. The diary is for nobody else to read, although it can be shared with the counsellor. The purpose of writing things down is to make them real.

Writing about trauma is very therapeutic in itself. It also provides a record of feelings and emotions so that when things look pretty low one can look back through the diary and realize that things were worse a few weeks ago (snakes and ladders again).

Diaries also help you to keep track of time. If PTSD is preventing you from working then you will have plenty of time on your hands. Having a diary will encourage you to complete some chores and make a note of your successes and your failures. It will help to give some structure to each day.

Counsellors may ask you to make lists. These lists may form the basis of the next counselling session. A list might itemize the people you are angry with. It might be the tasks that you have successfully completed in the last month. It could be a list of the times you have successfully conquered a fear or phobia.

Another task that might be set for you to complete is to write a 'fear script'. A fear script is quite simply a narrative of the traumatic event. Chapter 2 is a collection of fear scripts prepared by the 10 people who have volunteered their personal stories for this book.

The regular re-reading and re-writing of a fear script will, in time, make the event appear less traumatic to the writer. It is a way of placing events into a logical perspective.

CRISIS COUNSELLING

This is the term given to emergency counselling following a traumatic event. A crisis counsellor will usually only have one or two sessions with a sufferer with the aim of helping to establish that a trauma has taken place.[3] The crisis counsellor will have to help the sufferer answer vital questions:

Am I safe now?
What if I don't get better?
What is going to become of me?
What is or has been happening to me?

At the point of crisis the sufferer is too distressed and overwhelmed by events to begin any structured counselling course. The sufferer will need space to try to cope for themselves, but some gentle assistance with this coping may enhance the chances of swift recovery.

OTHER THERAPY

There are two other types of therapy likely to be offered to those who suffer with chronic PTSD: imaginal exposure and real-life exposure.

Imaginal exposure involves the sufferer imagining their trauma in great detail, using their own words. This should eventually be done in the first person, present tense, as if they were actually going through it all again. All five senses are used in imagining the trauma.[4]

This technique can be graded. This is done by using the least frightening of a number of images, or by using the third person, or past tense. Sessions should be audio-taped.

Some sufferers can become very distressed at the mere mention of any imaginal exposure procedure. (It terrified me!) The topic should not be explored in depth by the therapist until some level of trust and rapport has been established. Some sufferers are very resistant to the idea of making a tape of their trauma. This can be the case even with the safeguard that the tape will only be used in the counselling sessions.

David:
It all went pear-shaped when she ended the counselling session with the words '. . . and then we will start the graded imaginal exposure therapy'. Those few words were enough to start me sweating.

Once a tape has been made it should be played regularly as 'homework'. Often sufferers will want to remake the tape because they have left out aspects of the trauma. Care must be taken to limit the length of the tape. Too much information can make the tape last too long, and the therapy is then in danger of becoming a heavy burden. Tapes should be restricted to a maximum of 30 minutes.

It should be stressed that the first week of using imaginal exposure is usually the worst. It is much like the effects felt by a heavy smoker who gives up the habit. They experience increased tension, irritability and disturbed sleep. These returning symptoms may lead the sufferer to question why they are bothering with the therapy, particularly if they were feeling much better at the outset. It is vital for the therapist to confront the sufferer's doubts and assist in explaining why they feel so bad. Failure to do this may lead to the sufferer abandoning the treatment in the early stages. (*Remember the snakes and ladders.*)

After two to three weeks the sufferer should become more comfortable with the therapy. Like the ex-smoker, there will still be some discomfort, but it will be more manageable.

Sufferers may also be encouraged to experience graded real-life exposure to the trauma or to phobias which are triggers to flashbacks. Real-life exposure is exactly what it says. It is graded exposure to those things which provoke images of the trauma. This type of therapy is often offered to phobics and is now being offered to PTSD sufferers. However, there are some situations where real-life exposure is neither practical nor possible, and imaginal exposure will have to be used on its own.

Marlene:
The first stage of my real-life exposure was to take a ride in a cab. Simple really. It came around to my home address. My counsellor and I got in. We drove around the block and back to my home. The driver thought we were nuts. I spent most of my time with my eyes closed and concentrating on breathing in . . . 1 2 3 4 5 and then out again . . . 1 2 3 4 5 6. The trip lasted about four minutes.

This was an introduction to a real-life exposure treatment which was to last many weeks.

Marlene:
By the third week I was ready to go in the cab on my own. By this time I had told one or two of the drivers what I was up to. Instead of laughing at me, they took their role very seriously and were extremely supportive.
After my first 'solo' trip I was told by the driver, 'You did just great, lady,' and he actually reduced my fare.

The order in which imaginal exposure and real-life exposure is carried out must be discussed by the sufferer and therapist. There is no absolute rule about which should come first. However, it is generally felt that imaginal exposure should be started first. For reasons unknown, this exposure tends to help ease the depressive state of some PTSD sufferers and can improve their mood. Real-life exposure appears to be most effective with sufferers who are less depressed.

With all therapy of this type is it important to set targets and goals. In Marlene's case the goal was to feel comfortable when driven in a car by other people. She had been a passenger in both of the road accidents in which she was involved. Each week, Marlene set a target. 'By the end of this week, I shall have travelled in a cab for a 15 minute trip.' The targets were gradually extended until her goal was in sight.

Setting targets is important. There is also an element of risk attached to the practice. When targets are reached it feels marvellous. When you fail to reach targets it can be very depressing. Simple targets can sometimes appear unattainable.

Targets and goals must be set at realistic levels. What is realistic for a PTSD sufferer may appear ridiculously easy to anyone else – so what! Your targets must be achievable and worthwhile. Discuss your targets with your therapist.

Many PTSD sufferers complain that they are kept in the dark about their treatment. In the early stages this is probably quite reasonable. Life has become confused enough, and having some expert explaining theories of behaviour psychotherapy would be a total waste of everybody's time.

However, as time goes by it becomes important for someone to explain what has happened to you and how the damage to your emotions can be rectified. Therapists should take time to explain what they are doing and what they want you to do. Giving reasons for courses of action is important. Giving reasons for courses of treatment is vital if the treatment is to be followed through to its conclusion.

PTSD sufferers as a group are often hesitant when it comes to seeking treatment for their condition. The issues of distrust and loss of dignity appear to be intense. This is most common amongst the victims of violence – slightly less common in victims of natural disasters. Treatment must also have a high degree of acceptability to the victim. This acceptability is one of the main factors predicting a successful outcome.

Therapy offered by employers is often rejected by employees. This is particularly so amongst emergency service and armed service personnel. It appears to be largely a matter of trust. In particular, police officers are reluctant to trust counselling offered by the police service.[5] Many prefer to seek counselling from therapists with no direct link to the police. There is a fear that the confidentiality of the therapy is at risk if the counselled and the counsellor are employed by the same authority. This fear may be totally unfounded in almost all cases, but that fact does not dispel the fear.

Medication appears to be helpful in conjunction with psychotherapy because decreasing the sufferer's distress can make it easier for him or her to focus on the traumatic memories.

Finally, a significant number of PTSD victims predominantly suffer from physical symptoms. Unless these symptoms are assessed carefully by a medically trained person and an adequate reason is given for their presence, these victims are likely to reject any psychological treatment. Treatment of the physical symptoms is important.

PHYSIOTHERAPY

Many PTSD sufferers experience physical symptoms of the disorder. These symptoms require some form of physical therapy to ease them. Such therapy can be obtained from a physiotherapist, a chiropractor or a natural health practitioner.

The term 'physiotherapy' simply means the treatment of an injury by physical means such as manipulation, massage or exercise rather than by the administering of drugs. There is no reason why physiotherapy should not work in harmony with drug therapy and psychotherapy. Moreover, there is no reason why physiotherapy should not be used to alleviate the physical symptoms of an emotional condition such as PTSD. Unfortunately, not all practitioners of physiotherapy have come to appreciate the value their treatment can have for a PTSD sufferer.

Professional massage is a good treatment at any time. For the sufferer of PTSD, massage can help to relax muscles which have become tense and rigid. Back and neck massage can relieve these symptoms admirably. Massage of the limbs is also of benefit. Physiotherapists can offer massage as part of a course of treatment. Chiropractors can also offer a similar treatment. Those chiropractors trained in the McTimoney-Corley school adopt a very relaxed and stress-free form of massage designed to ease the whole body.

Exercise is important to everyone. Some victims of trauma may have physical injuries which require specific exercises. Those with no physical injuries can still benefit from a structured exercise regime designed to motivate them into positive thinking. Striving for improved physical fitness (even at a very moderate level) can boost self-esteem and aid recovery.

Physiotherapists have a wide range of electrical and mechanical machinery to assist the body in recovering from injury. One piece of equipment of significance to PTSD sufferers is a micro-electronic exerciser which provides interferential therapy.[6]

This method of treatment has been widely used for many years by the medical profession and is now being used to ease the symptoms of PTSD.

So how does it work? Normally, during physical exercise your muscles are caused to contract by electrical impulses transmitted from your brain. The interferential therapy involves two medium frequency currents used to produce a low frequency effect. An 'interference effect', equal to the difference in frequency between the two currents, is produced. At a frequency of 100Hz this has an analgesic effect, while at a lower 20Hz the treatment relaxes the muscles. A straightforward, natural, and extremely effective principle.

David:

I had not been sleeping very well since my assault. Then my physiotherapist suggested interferential. I was happy to try anything once. Two electrodes were placed at the bottom of my neck, and two more at the base of my spine. The machine was set at a very low frequency (20Hz) and I could feel a light tingling running up and down my back. The treatment lasted for 20 minutes. I fell asleep after just five.

By using very low frequency, intermittent alternating electrical currents, body tension and insomnia can be eased. The treatment will induce gentle relaxation of the body, soothing tension, easing muscular pain and creating a general feeling of well-being. Relaxation to aid sleep can be induced by the gentle, rhythmic pulses that are the essence of interferential treatment.

With interferential therapy there is no uncomfortable skin stimulation. It can be used as a treatment in its own right – but it is more commonly used in combination with other forms of treatment.

Paul:
I was so tense and worked up that the slightest noise made me jump violently. I found that interferential helped my body relax. Early on in my recovery it was the only treatment which enabled me to relax.

This treatment can be administered daily for 20-30 minutes. The results are quite simply amazing. Unfortunately, the treatment cannot be offered to pregnant women or anybody with a heart condition or with a pacemaker fitted.

The treatments described here are just a sample of the various types of physiotherapy available to PTSD sufferers.

RELAXATION

Time to relax is essential. Not just for PTSD sufferers but for everyone. The problem arises when people lose the ability to relax naturally. In an ideal world everyone would have a strategy to help them relax following times of stress or crisis. Time should be set aside for relaxation.

Sadly, we do not live in an ideal world and many of us have lost the ability to totally relax our bodies. Consequently, those of us who have experienced a traumatic, potentially life-threatening event will have to find ways of helping to ease the tension that comes with PTSD. We have to learn how to relax.

Aromatherapy can form part of a healing regime as well as being a preventive therapy in its own right. It gives pleasure through the sense of touch (massage), the sense of smell (aromatic oils), the sense of sight (pleasant surroundings), and sometimes through the sense of hearing (soft music). By so doing, it helps to create favourable conditions in body and mind for healing to take place quite naturally.[7]

It is not uncommon to find aromatherapy being used in hospitals as an aid to relaxation. Aromatic oils can be burned on special bedside burners, or mixed with a carrier oil and used in massage.

When using this therapy it is vital to find an aroma which you like. It is pointless to try to relax with a smell that you cannot tolerate. Perhaps the best natural oil for PTSD sufferers is neroli. This is distilled from the blossom of the bitter orange tree, although its scent is not at all citrusy. Unfortunately, it is expensive in its pure form, and some people do not like it anyway. Other aromas which have a good relaxing effect are camomile, coriander, geranium, jasmine, lavender, rose and citrus oils. These oils have proved to be useful in combatting depression and nervous conditions. They also help in alleviating insomnia and shock.

There are many commercial relaxation tapes available today. Most are a blend of gentle music and a calm voice instructing you to concentrate on picturesque scenes to let your mind drift into a daydream. They work. However, many PTSD sufferers are hypervigilant, and have a very poor level of concentration. These two symptoms of PTSD make learning to relax with audio-tapes a difficult, if not impossible, exercise.

Many PTSD sufferers find themselves with a lot of spare time on their hands. Many are not at work and will be at home, perhaps on their own, for much of the day. In these circumstances it is important to find some form of occupational therapy: to keep busy and to provide some purpose to living. People with nothing to do will soon become fed up and then depressed.

Occupational therapy does not have to be anything elaborate. Taking a general interest in gardening, jogging or cycling might be a start. Those who are less active physically may take up rug making, tapestry, fishing, reading or writing.

You must do something to occupy your time. If it can be a task with a goal, achieving that goal can be a great boost to your self-esteem. However, the therapy must be something which is realistic, something which is achievable in your present condition. If you are suffering from PTSD your memory may be impaired, your ability to concentrate will be reduced. Physically, your body may protest if you try to do too much, too soon. Being plagued with aching limbs or headaches which force you to abandon your chosen task will do nothing to improve your self-confidence. Choose your occupational therapy wisely.

There are other ways to relax. Perhaps you might like to try a sauna or a turkish bath. Either of these spa therapies will provide an atmosphere which is conducive to relaxation.

Chapter eight

<o>

PTSD in children

It is not only adults who suffer from Post-Traumatic Stress Disorder. The condition does not discriminate according to age. Of the death toll at Aberfan, 80 per cent were school children, and the survivors were also largely schoolchildren.

Aberfan is an important milestone in the study and understanding of disasters and how people can be affected by trauma. This was the first major disaster to be covered comprehensively by the medium of television. On Friday 21 October 1966 black and white television pictures of the school engulfed in a landslide were beamed into millions of homes throughout Britain. Instantly the name Aberfan was on everybody's lips. Few knew where it was, but that did not prevent them from being shocked by what they saw.

Twenty five years later, attention turned to Romania. Socially deprived, the country had placed all its eggs into one basket. Children were grouped together in institutions where they experienced 'concentration camp' style conditions in what were officially described as orphanages. As with Aberfan, pictures of this human disaster were screened in millions of households. This time the pictures were transmitted worldwide, in colour and with appalling vividness.

Children in the Third World were starving to death.

Matchstick limbs and bloated stomachs were almost impossible to comprehend. The pictures were there, however. The disaster was real. Children were suffering from, amongst other things, the effects of trauma.

Prior to Aberfan, children were unlikely to have witnessed the effects of any major traumas. Their learning had not included pictures which could shatter many dreams in an instant. They simply had no knowledge of this kind of suffering.

Children today are more worldly. They have read the books, seen the film clips and bought the fundraising T-shirt. Every child now has a memory of what a traumatic event can do. Their life experiences have been vastly increased by the media coverage of life-threatening events. This awareness may have a spiralling effect. The more children see trauma on television, the greater their perception of what might happen in a potentially life-threatening situation. Their illusion of safety has been steadily eroded over recent years.

The victims of major disasters can be subdivided into a number of groups:

Primary:	Survivors
Secondary:	Partners/Families
Tertiary:	Witnesses
Quaternary:	Emergency Service personnel

All four groups are 'at risk' of suffering from Post-Traumatic Stress Disorder. The first three groups are likely to include children. It is important that children's needs should be treated on an equal footing.

Many of the survivors at Aberfan were children.[1] They had lost friends and classmates. Teachers and the headmistress had also been killed. Somehow they had to pick up the pieces and continue with life.

In 1966, Post-Traumatic Stress Disorder had not been formally recognized. These children were officially suffering from shock. Fortunately the scale of the disaster had some benefits. The issues were not removed from the list of acceptable topics of conversation. Many of the villagers *wanted* to talk about the events of that one day. The topic was discussed quite openly and regularly. This was, perhaps, the first modern-day example of group therapy for patients who had suffered similar experiences.

There were reminders of the event all around the Welsh valley. The large grave. The devastated school. A population of children with entire age groups missing. The truth had to be faced, and by facing it together the community started to successfully rebuild itself.

Ten years after Aberfan, on the other side of the Atlantic, another group of school children were caught up in a traumatic event of a different kind. One hundred miles to the south-east of San Francisco lies the town of Chowchilla. On 15 July 1976 the school bus was hi-jacked and 26 children were kidnapped. The children (aged 5-14 years) disappeared for 27 hours. They were taken by three masked gunmen and transferred to a 'hole' which was a buried truck trailer. They were buried for 16 hours until two of the oldest and strongest boys managed to dig them out.

The children and parents were bombarded by the media.

A meeting was arranged for the parents and children at the medical health centre. At the meeting a physician predicted that only one of the 26 children would be emotionally affected by the experience. As no parent was willing to admit that their child was that 'one' there was a time lag of almost six months before parents asked for help and assistance.

A trauma specialist[2,3] offered limited crisis treatment to the parents of the Chowchilla children. After talking with each child, she concluded that every child showed signs of the emotional effects of psychological trauma. They were not identical to the symptoms of adult PTSD, but they were significant. Long after the kidnapping, 'fear of further trauma' continued to operate as a force behind 'fears of the mundane'.

Fortunately, incidents involving large numbers of children such as Aberfan (UK) and Chowchilla (USA) are extremely rare, but traumatic events in general are alarmingly frequent. Children are very often secondary or tertiary victims of PTSD, because another family member has been involved in a serious or life-threatening event, or because they have witnessed such an event. These categories of victims are frequently overlooked by the medical profession. The first stages of treatment for the primary victim may also provide opportunities for staff to make an initial evaluation of possible secondary and tertiary PTSD victims. Nursing staff in accident and emergency departments are particularly well placed to identify these potential victims.

In 1988 I was involved in the investigation of a fatal road accident in which two children were killed.[4] Whilst playing in a quiet residential street the children were unaware of the dangerous proximity of a street cleaning vehicle. The driver reversed into the two children, crushing them both.

Whilst pondering how I was to identify the two unfortunate playmates, I was aware of a teenage girl approaching the accident scene. She suddenly rushed forward and knelt beside the blanket which had been placed over the young bodies. Her movements were so quick that nobody reacted swiftly enough to stop her lifting a corner of the blanket. By the time she had been forcefully lifted away, she had inadvertently identified her brother and a cousin. Everyone around was deeply distressed by the incident and our hearts went out to this girl.

Six months later, I revisited the family and spoke to the girl's father. He still mourned the loss of his son, and explained that his wife and daughter could not bring themselves to talk to me. The girl was frightened of policemen. They were still deeply distressed by vivid flashbacks and nightmares about the accident scene. That one event occupied their thoughts for much of the day, even six months later. I did not have the courage to admit to them that the incident had also affected me greatly.

Children's responses to a traumatic event will depend upon a number of factors, such as age, cognitive level, understanding of the traumatic event, and their closeness to the event and the primary victim.

Characteristics of PTSD unique to children[5]

- Repetitive play containing themes about the traumatic event.
- Loss of recently-acquired developmental skills.
- Omen formation - a false belief in being able to predict future untoward events.
- Generalized fearfulness and separation anxiety.

Many characteristics of Post-Traumatic Stress Disorder are

exhibited by children who are taken into local authority care, although the term PTSD is rarely, if ever, applied to them. The fact that PTSD symptoms are manifested in these children is not surprising. The reasons for the care order are often linked to sexual or physical abuse, and to emotional and physical neglect. For children, this type of abuse and neglect is extremely traumatic and perceived as life-threatening. It has recently been argued that such victims of prolonged abuse are suffering from PDSD (Prolonged Duress Stress Disorder)[6], otherwise known as Rolling PTSD.[7] It is quite possible that the number of children PDSD sufferers exceeds the number of adult PTSD sufferers.

My own observations of foster children given into the care of my family has identified many instances of hyperalertness, sleep disorders, eating problems, regressive behaviour, self-abuse, uncustomary behaviour patterns and chronic anxieties. Many very young children taken into care will regress to drinking from a bottle and/or thumb sucking. Some three year-old children will regress in their play to activities normally associated with children a year younger. With careful planning, and plenty of tender-loving-care, this developmental lost ground can be speedily regained.

Every victim deserves good medical attention. Such medical attention should include help for any physical injuries, and possibly psychological counselling. Hospitals and accident departments can be very intimidating places for adults. This is even more true for children. Even though the medical staff are well-intentioned, some of their routine procedures and detailed history-taking can feel like a second episode of the trauma. Thus, when children first arrive at the hospital, a loved one should be permitted to stay with them at all times (including during x-ray procedures). A child victim will be feeling totally vulnerable and a family member or friend can be briefed to give tactful reminders when medical staff probe too deeply, too quickly.

Trust is especially important if a victim is to discuss the traumatic event. When a child victim does decide to disclose what has happened and to share the nature of the trauma, the trustee must *never* react with disbelief or belittling comments. Neither must the victim be treated patronizingly. Talking about trauma is vitally important and should be considered part of the medical care - not something staff enter into when there are slack moments.

Felicity:
It took me several weeks to build up towards telling someone about my brother. A couple of times I started to say something - but I got frightened that people would not believe me. Then I started to worry that I would be blamed. In the end, it was all too much and the truth burst out while I was having tea at a friend's house. Her parents were such understanding listeners. There were no awkward questions.

Simple and honest sharing of information will help the child cope, and will decrease any distorted perceptions of what has happened. However, it is NOT useful to make light of the event. If the event is perceived to be traumatic by the child involved − then traumatic it is.

The final task for medical staff is to provide guidance to the family concerning the child's possible reactions in the weeks and months following the traumatic event. A few minutes discussing the possible effects of the event will ease the worry when PTSD characteristics are identified.

Chapter nine

<o>

Personal stories
What happened to the ten cases?

Chapter 2 introduced ten victims of trauma and described the particular trauma they faced in their own words. Following on from that, many of the people have added comments at various points in the text to illustrate a variety of issues and problem areas.

Since their exposure to trauma, what has become of these people? How has their experience affected their life? Do they continue to suffer from Post-Traumatic Stress Disorder?

CASE 1: DAVID

I was attacked by a group of youths whilst on duty as a police officer. The attack left me with a broken cheek, a damaged kidney and spleen, and PTSD. The attack occurred in July 1990.

I spent five days in hospital after the attack. I thought I would start to feel better when I got home, but my own doctor started talking about Post-Traumatic Stress Disorder. He explained that my 'restlessness' was all due to the attack and that I was constantly re-living the incident in my mind.

I then started the counselling. At first it was at home

as I was in no fit state to travel. Then as the days went by I was asked to visit the hospital for my counselling therapy.

I was not sleeping, I was so jumpy it was ridiculous. I could not concentrate on anything for more than a few minutes, and my memory was terrible. I started to get flashbacks of the attack. They were very vivid pictures of the incident. I found them extremely distressing.

After two months it became obvious to me that I was not much better. I was then offered a stay at the police convalescent home. While I was there I met other PTSD sufferers and I started to gain a different perspective of the condition. I was introduced to aromatherapy, physiotherapy and hypnotism. I swam, exercised in a gym and relaxed in a sauna.

I returned home from convalescence realizing that it was possible to recover from PTSD but that it was going to take time. I had also accepted the fact that I was going to have to take some medication to help me combat the symptoms of the condition.

Nine months after the attack I returned to police duties. It was hard. So much had changed, even the station photocopy machine was in a different location. I was given a job in the training department, so had no direct contact with the public. I set to work at my new task.

I had been at work for just three months when my father-in-law died. This added extra strain to family life and affected me far more than I had expected. I had to take time off work. The week after his death was the first anniversary of my assault.

I went back to work briefly but found I had no

interest in what I was doing. I started to find excuses for finishing early. I had not told anyone, but in all my time at work I had avoided using a police radio. I also stopped using the telephone. This was making life very difficult.

By October 1991 I'd had enough of pretending. I had changed so much there was no way I could continue to work for the police. I was placed on sick leave pending retirement and was medically retired in April 1992.

Freed from the expectations of returning to police duties I started to make a better recovery. My sleeping improved but I was still troubled by my inability to use the telephone or to mix in crowded situations.

I started to write for magazines and newspapers. Nothing too spectacular, but one published feature tended to spark off another idea. By the end of the first 12 months I had been published in over 20 different publications both in Britain and the United States. I had also had a radio play produced in South Africa.

Much of my writing was linked to PTSD and my own experiences. As much as anything else it was therapeutic. I started to research the subject in university and hospital libraries, and I soon discovered that there was not much literature available to PTSD sufferers.

In April 1993, I agreed with Thorsons to produce a practical guide to PTSD sufferers. The project was to take up the next 15 months of my life, and help me to come to terms with the fact that the trauma of 1990 had permanently affected my life. But it had unknowingly provided me with the opportunity to do something I had wanted to do for many years - write.

CASE 2: MARLENE

Marlene had worked in the armed services and a hospital as a nurse and was no stranger to seeing casualties. Then she was involved in not one, but two motoring accidents. In both cases she was the innocent party and had no control over what happened. The accidents happened in December 1990 and January 1993.

After the first accident I spent two days in hospital and was then discharged. I was back at work within a month and thought very little about it.

The second accident was different somehow. It made me realize how lucky I was to be alive. My life had come so close to ending. I spent six days in hospital. For most of that time I was a wreck. I kept bursting into tears at the slightest thing. I could picture both accidents very clearly in my mind. Then the two started to blur together into one long incident. It was as if everyone on the road was out to get me.

When I was released from hospital I hated the journey home in my friend's car. I sat in my kitchen and remember thinking that I never want to go outside again. I couldn't bear the thought of walking along the street to the local store. I certainly did not want to drive there.

I relied a lot on friends helping me out. They got my groceries in for me and did all sorts of other chores. Then their patience started to wear thin. One or two stopped visiting.

One day I was standing at the window watching the rain. I remembered how heavy the rain had been that caused the first accident. Then I realized that it had been months since I had been out in the rain - I had been avoiding it.

My supervisor from work called to see me and she arranged for me to see a counsellor. The counsellor came to my home. I talked about the rain, about being a passenger in a car. I explained how frightened I was about going outside. Then I told her about the flashbacks I was having: the wakeful nights, the bad temper – the list of moans appeared to have no end.

By the time I had finished she was smiling at me. She said that what I was experiencing was all perfectly normal. I had survived two very traumatic events. On both occasions I was nearly killed. Naturally I was worried that the third time anything happened I would die. So to make sure I was safe, I stayed at home.

It all sounded so silly when she described it like that, but she was absolutely right.

Over the next weeks I saw a lot of my counsellor. She encouraged me to go out in a cab for a ride around the block. I panicked for most of the journey but when I got back home I felt so pleased with myself. The cab rides got longer and then I tried one on my own. Even the drivers were good to me. Nobody laughed. I remembered thinking that me and cars must be the same as Vietnam veterans and helicopters.

I kept a scrapbook of my thoughts and my steps to recovery. I also learned how to relax. I went to aromatherapy classes and found the sessions a great help. I immediately bought my own supply of oils and started to read up on the subject. Before I knew it, I was becoming an expert in aromatherapy.

The flashbacks diminished and my sleeping improved. I decided to give up nursing and went back to college to train as an aromatherapist. I could see my life in a totally new light.

By the end of 1994 I shall be set up in my own practice, teaching people the benefits of natural oils. I still remember the accidents as I drive my car along busy roads. The incidents have changed my life, but I'm enjoying almost every minute of it now.

CASE 3: JESSICA

Following her Caesarean section, Jessica and her baby daughter returned home. Jessica was in a terrible state. She suffered symptoms of agoraphobia and a fear of the telephone. But in 1981 very few people understood PTSD. Jessica was very much on her own.

I started having nightmares. These doctors with knives in their hands were walking towards me. I was terrified.

Every time the telephone rang I had a panic attack. I couldn't go outside for a walk because I thought these doctors would be waiting for me. I had my hands full looking after my baby.

I kept going back to my doctor. My husband made me go the first few times. The doctor said that I was depressed and that this was a normal reaction. He thought that I was disappointed at missing out on a natural birth.

I took tablets on and off for years. I went back to my part-time job when my daughter started school. It was a real struggle but I forced myself to do it.

Then one day my own doctor was on holiday and I saw somebody else. He suggested that I saw a psychologist which I agreed to do without giving it much thought. After a couple of discussions with the psychologist he suggested that I might be suffering from Post-Traumatic Stress Disorder. This was in 1988, seven years after my daughter was born.

The psychologist took me back in time and talked about my pregnancy and the birth of my daughter. I described the wait outside the theatre suite and how frightened I was. He said that most people were frightened of operations and that my extra wait outside the theatre had magnified my fears. He said that my reaction was normal.

My daughter is now studying for exams, and my husband and I are really contented with life. Now I know what my problems are, I am overcoming them steadily. Admittedly, I still take mild antidepressants from time to time. But I don't worry about taking them. I know they make me feel much better. I get out and about like everyone else and I use the telephone if I have to.

CASE 4: GRAHAM

Whilst travelling to an emergency incident in his Fire Chief's car, Graham found his role suddenly changed. One moment he was the rescuer, the next he was a victim. The brick which was thrown at his speeding car changed his life significantly.

After the 'accident' my memory became very vague. Now, I'm not sure how much I can remember and how much I have been told by other people. It is all one big jumble in my mind.

Because of my head and shoulder injuries, I was kept

in hospital for eight days. The incident made all the local papers and the TV news. I kept all the press cuttings but I hardly ever look at them. I will one day.

My recovery went well for three or four months. I returned to work, doing an office job as a senior Fire Prevention Officer. Then one day, I was asked to go to the scene of an incident and give advice to the crew who were dealing with it.

Speeding through the town with the blue lights flashing started to jolt my memory. I was on different roads, but every time I came to a bridge I slowed down and studied the area for would-be brick throwers. I got slower and slower. In the end I turned off the blue lights and pulled to the side of the road. I sat there and cried my eyes out.

It was as if the clock had been turned back four months. Everything was so clearly imprinted in my mind. I could see the brick coming towards my car - over and over again.

Eventually I realized they were calling me on the radio. I acknowledged the call and said I was having mechanical trouble. I found my way to the incident and got some questioning looks from one or two officers there. As soon as I could I went back to my office, hung up my uniform and went home.

I had two terrible nights when I just couldn't sleep. In the end I went to the doctor and said I had sleep problems and a lot of headaches. He talked to me for some time, asking all kinds of questions. I got very irritable with him; shouting and pacing up and down his office. Then I slumped down in the chair and cried again.

He told me what was wrong: Post-Traumatic Stress

Disorder. I thought that only affected people who were involved in large-scale incidents. He put me straight on a few things and explained how the drive under all those bridges in the Fire Chief's car had triggered off all the hidden memories of the trauma I had experienced: the incident in which I nearly died. He said I needed some time off work and gave me a certificate for *three months* sick leave!

Looking back at it all now, it was that long period of sick leave which made me realize that PTSD was not a two-minute illness. I was going to have to work at recovering from this condition.

I started going swimming. I went cycling. I went on long and lonely walks. I found myself doing all kinds of things so that I could be on my own. I distanced myself from the family and felt very numb. I rarely laughed, or cried. I just drifted in a world of my own.

After two months of this I agreed to see a counsellor. She had counselled me with many other firemen who had been diagnosed as suffering from PTSD. After lots of background questions she started to quiz me about the incident. I always tried to avoid the subject, but she carefully steered me back to it each time we met.

At about the same time I agreed to take some pills the doctor offered me. He explained that my body needed a break. I was stressed, very tired, very anxious and slightly depressed. I would need medical help to overcome this.

I was given a further three months off work.

My counsellor introduced me to three other people who were suffering from Post-Traumatic Stress Disorder. We met as a group on several occasions. It was such a relief to find that I was not alone with my problems -

other people who experienced totally different incidents appeared to suffer from the same symptoms.

I started to keep a diary. It was just a note of how I felt each day, what I did and what I postponed doing. I started to make myself do things so that I got out and met people. However, I got really sick of neighbours asking, 'How are you?' I'm sure they didn't really want to know. The trouble was, I had no visible means of being identified as ill. My injuries were invisible.

The Fire Service were very understanding about everything. There was no pressure to return to work before I was ready. The only pressure was from me. I felt guilty about not being at work.

My 50th birthday approached and I discussed with my wife the idea of taking early retirement. We had saved a considerable sum of money and had always wanted to move to Australia to live near our son and his family. We played around with the idea for several months before making the decision. It appeared that the incident had made both of us see life in a different way. We wanted to be positive about the future.

In the meantime, I had returned to part-time working in Fire Prevention. To be honest, I didn't do very much, but it kept me occupied. The counselling continued, but only once a month by this time. I kept in contact with the others in my counselling group. They were all making slow, but steady progress.

I retired in March 1993, 4½ years after the incident. We moved out to Australia and I now have a part-time consultancy job with a company selling fire equipment. I feel closer than ever to my wife, and we are living only 60 miles from the rest of our family.

When I look back on the incident now there is no

sorrow. It gave me the chance to think about the rest of my life and what I wanted to do. Occasionally, I have a sleepless night, and sometimes I panic slightly at the sight of a bridge. But I don't let these things bother me any more. I am too busy opening the shutters to each new day.

CASE 5: CINDY

For several months after the accident Cindy refused to admit to herself that anything was different. Having a ladder fall on you was no big deal, she would say. However, her friends knew differently. They saw the changes taking place in her character. The lecturers at college also noticed a difference.

I just wanted to pick up life where I had left off. I didn't miss much at college and soon caught up with the rest of the class. People kept inviting me out to parties, to music concerts and the like. I usually felt too tired and told them I suffered from headaches because of the accident.

I stopped colouring my hair and let it all grow. It was too much effort to keep the mohican style looking good.

Eventually my mum commented on the fact that I never went out any more. I thought about that. Mum was right. I was almost frightened to go out of the house. I even dreaded going to college. I was becoming agoraphobic.

I started to read up on phobias. It didn't really make sense. Mine was not an irrational fear, it was all due to that blasted ladder falling on me. Before that I was fine.

I started to get depressed. I also started to drink. I think dad noticed the drink disappearing, but he didn't say anything to me.

Then one morning they came home and found me drunk. Drunk at 11 a.m! Mum put me to bed and made all sorts of 'tut-tut'noises. The next day I made straight for the drinks cupboard, only to find it locked! I hunted high and low for the key but couldn't find it. I didn't even know what it looked like. Why had they locked it?

I knew the answer really, but couldn't bring myself to admit it. I sat and cried, then started to take stock of my life. My marks at college were steadily going down. One or two comments were made about that. I never went out. I drank too much and I was always moody.

Six months after the accident I had to return to hospital for a check-up. I sat in the out-patients department for ages waiting to be seen. It was very busy and I kept moving from seat to seat so as to stay away from other patients. I always sat with my back to a wall and never stopped watching the rest of the room. I started to think about the accident. I had changed since it happened. So what!

The doctor finally saw me. He looked shocked at the sight of me. Funny really because I looked more 'normal' at that time than at any stage in the last three years.

He started off by asking how long I had been drinking heavily. He said I was shaking badly and I stank of stale booze. Talk about being subtle. He just came out with it all.

After a few moments I started to unwind and tell him about the drink, about the quiet nights at home and the poor marks at college. I then waited for him to give me the 'pull yourself together' lecture, but it didn't come.

He started to ask all sorts of questions about my day-to-day life. I answered them without really thinking about what he was leading up to. He then asked me to wait as he wanted me to see another doctor.

The other doctor turned out to be a psychiatrist. I was livid. They thought I was nuts!

Eventually I calmed down. The psychiatrist started talking to me about the accident. I went through the whole story again. Then he asked why I never went out with my friends, and why I drank. I had to struggle to answer those. I didn't know myself.

At the end of all this he talked me into coming back in two days time to see a colleague of his. She would spend some time talking things through with me. In the meantime he wanted me to try to cut right down on the drinking.

It was not until the third meeting with the counsellor that the subject of Post-Traumatic Stress was mentioned. I had never heard of it, and so she explained that my agoraphobia, heavy drinking, depression and poor concentration at college were all linked to the accident. The tough bit was that I would have to stop drinking so that they could help me with all the other symptoms.

The counselling sessions progressed and the drinking eased and then stopped. It was hard going, though. Eventually I told my parents what was happening. They were so relieved. It transpired that they knew I was not well but that every time they said anything I just bit their heads off. They were worried that I would leave home, or 'do something silly' because I was clearly feeling very fed-up. Being honest with my parents made everything else so much easier to deal with.

The counselling worked out and the phobic behaviour improved. I stopped drinking. My dad took me out to a pub for a drink. We went into the crowded bar and I ordered a fruit juice. When we came out I was so excited with the achievement that I'm sure everyone else thought I was drunk. My dad just grinned from ear to ear.

Things progressed steadily. I finished college with the required piece of paper and got a job not too far from home. I now have a boyfriend, and things in that department are pretty serious. We are planning a honeymoon in Florida.

CASE 6: MATTHEW

The suicide of his closest friend, followed by a burglary in his own home drastically affected Matthew. It is not easy to establish which event induced the PTSD, and so it was assumed that both occurrences were equally to blame.

I found John's suicide very difficult to cope with. For weeks I held myself responsible. I should have noticed how depressed he had become. I didn't.

I saw John and myself as very much alike. We were almost like brothers. We did everything together. I missed him terribly.

The burglary was the trigger that sent my mind racing back to John's death. Slowly I realized that what had really frightened me was the thought that John had been murdered and that the killer might still be in the house waiting for me. When I was burgled, this all came back to me and I thought that the murderer had returned for me.

It all sounds so silly now. But months of careful counselling brought all this out into the open. When I was a kid, someone in our street was shot dead. I saw the body in the street before the police arrived. Clearly, the closeness of these deaths had an effect upon me. The more I think about it the more convinced I become that the brain has got a separate mind of its very own. It stores things for years.

I started to become very depressed - really low. I never actually tried to kill myself, but I think I came close to it on a few occasions. The depression eased with medication. However, it was replaced by the side-effects of the drugs. My doctor tried me on five different types of antidepressant before he found one that I could live with.

I have been taking these tablets for two years now. Soon I will have to start reducing the doses and seeing how I feel. I tried once before and the depression returned.

I also suffered a lot from panic attacks. I found public transport the worst. You can never be in control of the situation on public transport. When I visited Europe I was really pleased with myself for coping on the airliner. Then the incident on the London Underground blew all that confidence away.

I am slowly learning to control the panics. Sometimes I do so by simply avoiding the situation, but more and more I am prepared to try things to see if I can cope. I remember the analogy of the snakes and ladders board, and that helps me overcome the failures. There is always the next time.

Since the burglary I have changed jobs three times. I don't find it easy to settle into new situations but I am sure that, too, will improve given time.

Even all this time after John's death, different things spark off the memory of the day I broke into his home. Each time a dog barks I think of John's dog. When the telephone rings I often think of my search for John's telephone. When I hear glass breaking (usually a TV sound effect) I recall how I broke into John's home. All these triggers make it difficult for me to relax during the day. I am always alert and waiting for the next event to spark off a memory.

Looking back through my diaries I can see that I have improved considerably over the last two years. Although events still spark off sad memories, they do not spark off the awful panic attacks I used to have. Probably those around me are totally unaware that I am panicking about something. I relax myself by concentrating on my breathing and letting my arms hang loose.

I am sure that, given a little more time, continued guidance from my counsellor, and the maintained support of my doctor that I will crack this PTSD. The memory of John's death will always be with me. But when I think of him I also remember all the good times.

CASE 7: RICHARD

Following a fire which threatened to destroy an entire family, Richard found that reminders of the event prevented him from doing his job as a police officer effectively. This was a problem he had to overcome.

I returned to work two days after the fire. It was all I could think about. Pictures of it kept filling my mind. It was impossible to last a day at work without something reminding me of the way those people were nearly burned alive before my eyes.

August is usually a social amble from one barbecue to another. But this year I just couldn't stand the sight and smells and had to walk out of friend's homes on several occasions. My wife got pretty sick of this and told me so in no uncertain terms. I explained the reasons behind it and she stared at me in horror. I then told her about the fire in detail. She only knew what she had read in the papers and most of that was rubbish.

The police training exercise where I had a row with the instructor was the last straw. I knew I needed help to overcome this thing, but there was no way I was going to tell anyone in the police what was troubling me.

I saw a trauma counsellor and she started to put everything into perspective for me. It had taken five months for me to make the appointment, however, and in that time I had started to totally avoid situations that I knew would remind me of the fire. Now I find that these avoidances had become habits that were difficult to break.

Initially, having the counselling brought all the flashbacks back as vividly as ever. The counsellor said this might happen and that, although painful, it was a good indication that I had started to deal with the trauma. However, I found that the return to these vivid images depressed me and made me anxious that I might never get any better.

Going over the details of the fire with my counsellor was painful, but it started to work for me in the end. I could picture the family trapped behind the bars at the window without panicking – after all, I knew that they got out safely so why did I need to panic?

I felt that I had a terrible lack of confidence. I lost the ability to accept normal negative events, and looked for occasions where I had failed. I started to see my failings all around. Nothing I appeared to do had any positive slant to it. I became over-critical of myself. This started to rub off on my wife, and she started to lose confidence in the strength of our relationship. I think that I cut her out of this period of my life.

As I began to feel better, the depression gradually lifted and life started to feel better. I moved to a different department within the police and that made my life easier. People were not always asking after my health (something I hated) and I slowly started to put the event behind me.

The first anniversary of the fire was hard. It was in the news once again and I found my thoughts drifting back to the scene of the blaze. I got over that little setback, however, and life continues.

I think above everything else the event taught me a great deal about life. I now look more for the good in everything instead of looking at the bad side of things. I also count my blessings. I think of all the things I have, and I value them. Most of all, I value my family and friends. In a strange way the incident has brought us all closer together, we are more honest about our feelings and we have no secrets from each other.

Not only that, but this year I have been promoted!

CASE 8: FELICITY

Felicity is now in her final year at school. In the four years since she was first assaulted by her brother she has endured much. There is little doubt that her story has been repeated in other family situations all around the world.

Soon after I told my friend's parents what had been happening I moved away from my parents and was fostered by a family in another county. I felt very tense and it was some time before I made any friends at my new school. When I did, they wanted to know why I had moved away from my parents and why I was living in a foster home.

I told them my mum was dead and my dad was in prison. That lie came easier than the truth.

In fact my parents kept in touch with me for a while. My brother still lived at home and they could not believe that what I was saying could possibly be true. They thought I had made it all up because I was jealous of my brother. I told them that it was impossible for me to come back home while my brother lived there and that if they didn't believe me that was their problem – not mine.

Sleeping was my problem. I hated to have the bedroom door shut, so it was agreed that I could leave it wide open every night. The trouble was I often had nightmares that woke up the rest of the household. My foster father would wake me, give me a drink and hope that I would fall back to sleep. I used to lie on the bed and watch the clock during the early hours of the morning. No way could I get back to sleep.

One day at school we had a talk about drug abuse. A police woman gave the talk. I was sure that she knew I had been arrested for smoking stuff. At the end of the talk she looked right at me and smiled. I was convinced she knew all about me.

That night I didn't go back to my foster family. I walked for hours and was eventually picked up by a police car at 2 a.m. I sat in the back of the car terrified. They just took me back to my foster home though. They were all very nice and nobody shouted at me.

The next day, I told my foster mother about the talk at school and what I thought the police woman knew. She gave me a hug and made us a drink. She explained that she knew all about what had happened to me and that if I wanted to, I could talk at any time. That was such a relief.

We talked on many occasions after that. It was great to have someone to talk to. Someone I could trust totally. My nightmares became less frequent and my school work started to improve. I actually got some good exam results, much to many people's surprise.

Occasionally, I still feel a little awkward when anyone accidentally touches me or tries to hug me. It reminds me of my brother and all the horrible things in my past.

When I see pictures of children in other countries who are struggling to survive I still feel some kind of bond with them. It sounds silly, but I feel that I can appreciate and understand how they must be feeling. I know some girls have pictures of pop stars on their bedroom walls. In my bedroom I have a collection of Oxfam posters of children suffering in the poorest areas of the world.

I hope that my exam results will be good enough to get me a place at university next year. I'm still not sure what I want to do as a career, but I expect it will be something to do with children.

CASE 9: PAUL

Unlike the other victims in this book, Paul's trauma was very well publicized by the media. It was a national disaster, and that factor added to the problems of recovery.

The week after the disaster was hell. There were pictures on the television and in the newspapers. Journalists were pestering for a good story. Nobody appeared to appreciate that I wanted to be on my own, and at home. In the end I went to stay with my parents in Surrey.

I was haunted by the memories of the incident. In just 60 seconds the ship went over, the lights went out and the water came in. Nearly 200 people died and I am sure I climbed over some of the bodies in order to save myself.

Physically and emotionally I was in a real state. I was suffering with tiredness, sleeplessness, bad dreams, loss of concentration, dizziness, shakes, muscular tension, headaches and backache. My broken arm gave me no real trouble.

I was visited by a social worker who said she was part of the 'away team' working with disaster victims. As I didn't actually live in Kent, I was being treated by her team. Although there were only 350 survivors of the disaster, my social worker said they were expecting to deal with around 10,000 people who had been affected in some way by the trauma. That included families and those involved in the rescue. This statement made me appreciate the scale of the event I had been caught up in.

After three weeks I returned to work. Everyone there wanted to know all the details. I found myself recounting my escape time after time. I made the story very unemotional - just as it was when I gave my statement. I left out the screams and the pushing and barging of frightened people clambering to get free.

One or two people saw through me I think. They saw that there was more to it than I was telling.

The social worker became my counsellor and I saw her regularly. It was her idea that I should have more time off work, and my own doctor readily agreed to this. I simply couldn't concentrate on anything. I made lots of mistakes. My colleagues covered most of these for me, but I think they were relieved when I said I was having more time off.

At my parents' home, time dragged. The nightmares persisted and I started to shut everyone out of my life. I went on long walks, often just sitting on park benches and letting my thoughts drift back over the disaster.

I started to picture the faces of other people around me before the ship went over. I didn't know what had become of them. I started to feel guilty that I had survived while some of them had died. Then I felt ashamed of the fact that I may have climbed over their bodies to escape. I couldn't get these pictures out of my mind.

I'm not sure when I reached the lowest point after the disaster. It was about six weeks after the event I think. I thought I had flu. I just wanted to go to bed and die. My parents' doctor then announced that I was depressed and was suffering from Post-Traumatic Stress Disorder.

It was such a relief to hear that I was normal, and that what I was experiencing was a very normal reaction to an event that had almost killed me. That knowledge helped me no end.

I could now see a point to the counselling. I was keen to tell everything – what I did, how I felt and what was worrying me. It was such a weight off my mind to be able to talk about it all. I stopped feeling ashamed.

I took five months off work in all. When I returned many things had changed but I was prepared for that. I had changed, too. I worked steadily until the first anniversary of the disaster. That was a difficult time and I had to take a few weeks off again. Nobody seemed to mind that. They were very understanding.

I spent that time with my parents. We talked about the disaster. For the first time, we really talked about it. They told me about the news flashes. The horror when they realized that I was on the ship that was sinking – the ship they were watching on television. For the first time I was aware of the fact that they had been victims too. That sharing of knowledge brought us all much closer together.

It is all behind me now. I shall never forget it, but I can now live more easily with the memories. It was four years before I ventured onto a ship again. That was a big day for me. It was the final hurdle along my road to recovery.

IMPACT OF LIFE EVENTS QUESTIONNAIRE

Date: 1 Nov 1993

NAME   PAUL

ON   6 March 1987   YOU EXPERIENCED   a ship sinking

Below is a list of comments made by people after stressful life events. Please check each item, indicating how frequently these comments were true for you DURING THE PAST SEVEN DAYS. If they did not occur during that time, please mark the 'not at all' column.

	FREQUENCY			
	Not at all	Rarely	Sometimes	Often
I thought about it when I didn't mean to.		✓		
I tried to remove it from my mind.	✓			
I had waves of strong feeling about it.		✓		
I had dreams about it.			✓	
I stayed away from reminders about it.		✓		
I tried not to talk about it.		✓		
Pictures about it popped into my mind.	✓			
Other things kept making me think about it.		✓		
I tried not to think about it.			✓	
Any reminders brought back feelings about it.			✓	
My feelings about it were kind of numb.	✓			
Thoughts about it prevented me from sleeping.			✓	

CASE 10: CHRISTINE

Christine was raped. She was raped by somebody she knew and respected. About 50 per cent of rape victims suffer PTSD symptoms. The experience affected not just Christine, but her family too.

By the time my husband and two daughters had returned home from their swimming session I had showered, cried, showered again, dressed and got halfway through my third brandy.

I told my husband that I'd had a row with one of the senior partners at work. I said my job was on the line and that I didn't really want to talk about it just now. I could see he didn't believe me, and I'd never lied to him before but I simply could not tell him the truth, yet. By the morning I would feel better. I had another shower before I went to bed.

The following day I phoned in sick. My head was splitting as a result of too much brandy. My legs were like jelly and I felt like a tramp. By 8.45 a.m. I had the house to myself.

I couldn't stand being alone in the house. All my senses appeared to go into permanent alert as if the danger might return at any moment.

I worked my way through a whole packet of cigarettes and drank mugs of steaming coffee. Every time there was a noise in the house, I jumped out of my skin. By mid-afternoon I was a total wreck. I went to the police.

During the next couple of weeks I had to undergo interviews and statement-taking that appeared endless. I had to tell my husband, and he was just great. Once he got over the initial desire to go around and thump the culprit he was wonderfully supportive to me.

I had a medical examination and a pregnancy test. More questions to answer – then nothing. Week after week of nothing. It was as if everybody had forgotten the rape, except me. I still couldn't sleep, I kept seeing the inside of his room and that horrible smile of his.

Our own lives resumed. Sex was difficult for me at first, but tender love and care from my husband eased my anxiety. God, how lucky I am to have him.

During the day I became terribly irritable. My work suffered because I couldn't concentrate for long. I also had problems remembering things. I had to write down everything in my diary. I'd told my senior partner what happened. He had trouble believing it, but went along with what I told him. It certainly explained the way my work had gone downhill.

Then one day he asked me into his office. He said that he had spoken to Dr xxxxx and that my story was a pack of lies. He'd been told that my attacker and I had been intimate on a number of occasions and that suddenly I'd had a change of heart about the relationship. I was horrified!

That was my last day at work.

I became depressed and anxious about our family's financial situation. My company car had gone and I was going to find it difficult to find a similar job in such a rural area. Everything looked grim.

It was my husband who found the solution. 'Leave things for a while and then set up on your own.' It sounded mad to start with, but the more I thought about it the better I liked the idea. It was what I had always wanted to do. The timing was forced upon us to some degree, but I had no doubt that I could make a success of things given half a chance and a few good clients.

Looking back at things now, that was the turning point in my recovery. It is over two years since I was raped. I have now been self-employed for just a couple of months as it took a while to get things organized. I work as much as my recovery permits me. We are not rich, but neither are we bankrupt. I still don't always sleep well, but that isn't too bad.

Recently, when my daughter caught me singing in the bath, she asked, 'Are you better now?' I wonder how much they understand about all this.

The police dropped all charges and explained that they were unlikely to get a prosecution. I thought I would be angry, but it was a relief in a way. I just want a chance to re-build my own life again. I want to look to the future.

IMPACT OF LIFE EVENTS QUESTIONNAIRE

Date: 8 Nov 1993

NAME   CHRISTINE

ON   3 September 1991   YOU EXPERIENCED   rape

Below is a list of comments made by people after stressful life events. Please check each item, indicating how frequently these comments were true for you DURING THE PAST SEVEN DAYS. If they did not occur during that time, please mark the 'not at all' column.

	FREQUENCY			
	Not at all	Rarely	Sometimes	Often
I thought about it when I didn't mean to.	✔			
I tried to remove it from my mind.			✔	
I had waves of strong feeling about it.			✔	
I had dreams about it.			✔	
I stayed away from reminders about it.	✔			
I tried not to talk about it.			✔	
Pictures about it popped into my mind.		✔		
Other things kept making me think about it.	✔			
I tried not to think about it.		✔		
Any reminders brought back feelings about it.			✔	
My feelings about it were kind of numb.	✔			
Thoughts about it prevented me from sleeping.			✔	

Chapter ten

◀◉▶

Legal actions

The legal system can be an asset to victims of trauma in much the same way as therapists and friends. Victims turn to the legal system for redress from any physical or psychological injuries that have been inflicted on them.

Many victims will already have some general knowledge of the legal system, but there are experts in the field who are trained to help serve the needs of victims. Their title varies from country to country; in the USA the group is called VAP (Victim Assistance Programme) while in the UK a similar organization is called Victim Support. Consult your local branch.

Some victims may turn to their own legal adviser for assistance.

After the disaster at Aberfan, no one sued for psychological shock, even though many parents not only lost their children but saw them dead. Following the Buffalo Creek disaster of 1972, lawyers started to examine the possibility of claiming compensation for psychological injuries. Prior to that, legal actions were restricted to claims for physical injuries and loss of earnings.

Compensation is not the primary worry of PTSD victims in the first instance. Immediately after any traumatic, potentially life-threatening event, comes the trauma of making statements. Victims of motoring accidents are expected to make witness statements. Victims of assaults are expected to make a statement as an aggrieved party to the event.

Making a statement can be as traumatic as experiencing the event itself. There is a variety of views about how, and when, a statement should be taken. One school of thought is that any statement should be taken as soon after the event as possible. By doing this, the memories are as fresh as they can be and they are unlikely to be affected by other people's views of the incident.

The other viewpoint is that some people are not emotionally ready to think their way through the event and provide a statement for several days – maybe weeks. A few people may never feel able to provide a statement.

Statements are required for a variety of reasons: to establish that a crime has been committed; to identify a guilty party; to provide evidence as to the precise cause of death of any victims. It follows, therefore, that the evidence obtained within a statement may be used at criminal proceedings, in civil courts and at inquests into the event.

The form that any proceedings will take depends upon the country in which the event occurred. In instances where the event has occurred between international boundaries, at sea and in the air, the venue for any legal proceedings has to be mutually agreed according to international conventions. Whatever the location of proceedings there are some areas of common ground.

CRIMINAL PROCEEDINGS

Many physical and sexual assaults will result in criminal proceedings being taken against the assailant. As the victim of the assault, a PTSD sufferer is likely to be the primary prosecution witness. Even if the PTSD sufferer is a witness to the trauma, the existence of Post-Traumatic Stress indicates that what the witness saw was fundamental to the case.

The matter does not end with the dictation of a witness statement. The victim may be asked to formally identify the accused. A second, or even third, statement may be needed. Eventually, a court appearance may be required.

Appearing in court requires careful preparation. It is a difficult and stressful ordeal for anyone. For a PTSD sufferer it can be very intimidating. Build up to the court date together with your counsellor. Go through the event thoroughly, and restrict yourself to what *you* can remember. Try to block out what you have subsequently been told by others.

If possible, visit the court before the date of the trial and familiarize yourself with the surroundings. Knowing where the witness box is located in relation to the rest of the room will help you prepare for the occasion.

If it is all too much for you, discuss the matter with your doctor. If he agrees that attending court will adversely affect your condition he will provide the court with a letter to that effect. If this happens the court will either adjourn the hearing to a later date, or proceed without your verbal evidence. Clearly, your non-attendance may weaken the prosecution case, but if the trauma of the event has adversely affected your health once, there should be no reason for it to adversely affect your recovery, too.

At the end of the hearing, the issue is not over. Either side may appeal to a higher court if the outcome is not what they expected. Such an appeal may mean that you will have to go through the whole thing again.

For some years now, it has been acknowledged that rape victims have an arduous time at court; so merciless, that a large number of victims decline to attend court at all. What is true for rape victims is also true for a considerable number of victims of trauma. Unfortunately, many courts fail to treat PTSD sufferers with the sympathy they deserve.

What is true for criminal cases is also true for motoring offences which result in a court hearing. Witnesses and victims will be dragged through the same procedures.

CIVIL PROCEEDINGS

Cases which are brought before civil courts start off in much the same way as criminal proceedings. There are two significant differences. First, the timespan between the original event and the final court hearing is likely to be far greater in a civil case. It is not unlikely that the civil hearing will take three or more years to reach the court room.

Second, the level of proof required in a civil case is different from that required by criminal courts. Criminal courts demand that the case be proved beyond reasonable doubt. In civil courts the law demands that the case be proved on the balance of probabilities. In other words, if a person or company is 51 per cent to blame, that is enough for a civil court to prove the case.

Because of this difference in the level of proof required, civil proceedings tend to linger on and on as lawyers debate the issues they intend to present at court.

This delay in the proceedings may be seen as a blessing by those who are dreading the day that they have to attend court and give their evidence. However, the long delay can work against the victim's interests by dragging up past events, which have already been successfully dealt with during counselling sessions and filed away in the recesses of memory. In consequence, some people who had previously thought they had 'recovered' from the trauma may find some of the old symptoms recurring for a time. This would be quite a natural reaction, and one that witnesses should be prepared for.

INQUESTS AND ENQUIRIES

Inquests are probably the most stressful proceedings to have to deal with. The investigation to verify why somebody died is always going to cause distress. It is necessary to hold an inquest, not only to establish a cause of death, but to look at the details of the incident and see that future incidents of the same nature can be avoided.

In those cases where there were no fatal injuries, an enquiry may be set up to work in the same way as an inquest, to try to prevent the trauma being repeated in the future.

Many victims of traumatic events have feelings of guilt. They feel guilty that they might not have acted correctly in the few seconds when the incident occurred. They feel guilty that they survived while others may have perished. They feel guilty for having survived.

It is never easy to give evidence in court. To give your evidence while you have feelings of guilt can be very traumatic. These feelings should be worked through during counselling sessions before the court hearing. They are erroneous feelings which are one of the symptoms of post-traumatic stress. No matter what the situation, nobody has the right to criticize another person for anything they did, or didn't do, during a few seconds when they thought their own life was at risk. In 999 times out of 1,000 these feelings of guilt are totally unfounded. In the remaining cases they are simply unreasonable.

COMPENSATION

In the USA, since the Buffalo Creek disaster, the idea of Post-Traumatic Stress Disorder has been accepted by the courts. It is now routine for disaster victims, whether they are survivors or the bereaved families, to receive substantial psychological damages running into millions of dollars.

In Europe, courts have been slower to accept this concept. Survivors of the Bradford Football Stadium Fire (1985) received no compensation for psychological damages. Passengers on *The Herald of Free Enterprise* (like Paul), which sank in 1987, had their claims for compensation finally settled by an arbitration panel. Paul received a fixed payment of £5,000 plus £5,000 for physical injuries and £24,000 for psychiatric injuries.

Many PTSD sufferers may find that they have a case for claiming compensation. How they set about making that claim will depend upon how their 'invisible injuries' were caused. However, the road to compensation is a long and winding one. The journey drags on for years and many sufferers decide to forget the whole thing and get on with the rest of their lives long before any offer of compensation is made. Others may, for the same reason, accept the first offer that is made – in order to put the experience behind them.

Whether or not to pursue compensation for your injuries is a personal decision. Do not make the decision too soon after the incident. The full impact of the trauma may not be apparent for several months. On the other hand, don't leave the decision too long. In many instances there is a time limit of three years, after which it is deemed too late to apply for compensation.

For many victims there is a very legitimate desire for compensation. Because an injustice has been done to them they naturally feel entitled to some form of compensation. The quest for compensation is often an important part of recovery. At the same time, this quest may prevent sufferers from facing the full reality of what has happened to them. For many, there can be no adequate compensation.

MEDICALS

Many people who are injured have to attend medical boards to be assessed as to their rate of recovery. This is true of PTSD sufferers too.

The assessment may be needed by your employer, or a government department, or a doctor wanting a second opinion. The medical results may be required by a court as evidence of your condition. Whatever the reason, many PTSD sufferers can expect to attend a string of medical examinations.

Now, if you had a broken leg or damaged hearing, it would be a relatively simple task to examine you and assess how well your recovery was progressing. Because you are suffering from PTSD that assessment is far more tricky.

Medical examinations are often structured in the same way for every single client who attends. In consequence, the PTSD victim often attends a medical and is measured, weighed, and asked to provide a urine specimen.

Why?

Because that is what it says on the form!

It may appear to be a very minor point, but a PTSD victim is not going to be very impressed by a medical which begins with a urine sample. It suggests that those doing the assessment have no real idea of what PTSD is all about. If handled badly, such a medical can quickly degenerate into a battle between the patient and the doctor.

At these medicals, the examiners must trust the patient to tell them the truth about their condition. For months during treatment and counselling the sufferers have had to trust the counsellors and therapists. The medical is a time when the need for trust is reversed.

The only way a PTSD victim can be medically assessed is to be interviewed by someone qualified in the field of PTSD. The interview, or discussion, should be relaxed and as casual as possible. It should not feel like an interrogation, or like a cross-examination in the witness box. The patient should not feel as though he or she is on trial.

Many medicals which assess PTSD rely on the tests described in Chapter 6 of this book. By giving the patient a variety of tests and comparing the results with those of earlier tests it is relatively easy to assess the patient's progress. However, because of the very nature of PTSD and any associated feelings of anxiety and depression, test results may vary, even from day to day.

PTSD AS A LEGAL DEFENCE

PTSD victims frequently suffer from flashbacks and from an exaggerated startle response. These two symptoms of the condition make them very 'jumpy' at times. It is hardly surprising therefore, that some PTSD victims have been guilty of crimes themselves. There have been instances of assault, robbery and even murder which, it is claimed, are indirect results of suffering from PTSD.

Marlene:
I learned about a combat veteran who heard a helicopter overhead in civilian life and had a flashback to the war itself. He stabbed a neighbour because he momentarily saw the neighbour as 'the enemy'. He was later convicted of assault.

There have been several instances where PTSD victims have reverted to their 'traumatized personality' and committed a crime which, a few moments later, they cannot even remember.

Matthew:
After the incident on the London Underground, I panicked for weeks. I knew I should not have hit the drunk, but I had no control over my actions for those few seconds. Luckily for me, I heard no more about the incident.

Cases such as these are coming before the courts more frequently. Each case must be treated on its own merits as courts struggle to interpret recent findings in human behaviour in a way that brings justice to both aggressor and aggrieved.

WARNING

Untreated victims of PTSD, or those who are not fully recovered, are prone to intrusive memories and sudden flashbacks of the traumatic event. Standing in a witness box, hostile cross-examination may act as a trigger to the body's emergency mobilization systems and may cause the victim to re-experience the terror of the original traumatic event.

I attended court 10 months after my assault but I believe that the court hearing, and meeting my assailants face-to-face, pushed my recovery back many more months.

Each PTSD sufferer must consider the issues involved in turning to the legal system for support. This is not in any way suggesting that the legal system be avoided, but only that victims make informed choices about what to do. Courts can be helpful, but in many instances the rights of assailants still take precedence over the rights of the victim. **Courts have a duty to protect the innocent, but because of this duty innocent victims do not always receive justice.**

Chapter eleven

Back to the future

Most books and reports on Post-Traumatic Stress Disorder avoid looking into the future on behalf of PTSD victims. That is probably because the final chapter is by far the hardest to write – so little is understood.

Some people will make a swift and steady recovery. Many will recover in a series of stages, a long painful progress with milestones of both successes and failures. A handful may never fully recover, but their ability to cope with the symptoms will strengthen and grow as time passes. The human race has survived so far because people are adaptable. What PTSD does is to force change upon its victims too quickly - so time *will* heal.

To help illustrate different points in the text, 10 cases have been reported, with insights from the 10 adding to the general comments made. By way of conclusion, all were asked to comment on their present state of recovery and to use the snakes and ladders board as a guide to that recovery.

HAVE THE TEN CASES RECOVERED?

David — Retired from the police 20 months after the incident and now writes for a living. Suffers with some symptoms occasionally. On square 97.

Marlene — Left nursing to return to college, and is now a trained aromatherapist. On square 98.

Jessica — Late in diagnosis, it has been a struggle but the end is now in sight. On square 85.

Graham — Retired 4½ years after the incident and moved to Australia. Still has occasional feelings of depression. On square 95.

Cindy — Now married, and enjoying her work. Still refuses to drink alcohol. On square 99.

Matthew — After three job changes, he has still to settle. Life is still very difficult. On square 75.

Richard — Now promoted within the police after a change of duties. On square 99.

Felicity — Not finding it easy to form relationships, and still very much on her guard. On square 90.

Paul — Has recovered well, but feels that life will always be that little bit different. On square 95.

Christine — Occasionally moody, but her move to self-employment is working out fine. On square 97.

It can be seen that none of the ten will admit to reaching the last square on the board (100) but that all have made good progress. They all had to start at square one.

The journey over the remaining squares may take many more months, or it may finish tomorrow. But the nearer each person gets to that final square, the fewer snakes lie in their pathway.

Snakes and Ladders Game

FINISH 100	Cindy Richard 99	Marlene 98	David Chr'tine 97	96	Graham Paul 95	94	93	92	91
81	82	83	84	Jessica 85	86	87	88	89	Felicity 90
↑ 80	79	78	77	76	Matthew 75	74	73	72	71
61	62	63	64	65	66	67	68	69	↑ 70
↑ 60	59	58	57	56	55	54	53	52	51
41	42	43	44	45	46	47	48	49	↑ 50
↑ 40	39	38	37	36	35	34	33	32	31
21	22	23	24	25	26	27	28	29	↑ 30
↑ 20	19	18	17	16	15	14	13	12	← 11
START 1	2	3	4	5	6	7	8	→ 9	↑ 10

All PTSD sufferers have experienced a traumatic, potentially life-threatening event. That experience needs to be re-experienced in order to relate properly to each aspect of the trauma. You need to find out what frightened you.

The counselling process helps sufferers work through this trauma in much the same way as people need to grieve for a loved one who has died. At the end of any period of grieving, the person you loved is still dead. However, you have learned to cope with that death, that loss, and to rebuild your life without that person around you. Recovery from PTSD is much the same. You will never forget the trauma, but you will eventually rationalize the memory of the event so that you can think about it without having to relive it. Once you reach this stage of recovery you will have control over your past, rather than allowing your past experience to control you.

As with grieving, the turning point in recovery is reached when you realize that something in your life has changed permanently. You cannot turn the clock back and pray that the traumatic event never occurred. Its memory will remain and you have to master that memory.

It may be that you have to visit two or three counsellors before you meet a person you can openly discuss your situation with, someone with whom you feel most comfortable. Remember that counselling *will* raise painful issues for you. You must remind yourself not to drop out of treatment when the going gets tough. Too many PTSD sufferers fail to complete their treatment because the treatment has not been properly explained to them from the start. Ask questions of your counsellor.

During counselling, many sufferers take their thoughts back to their childhood. Memories which were presumed lost are rediscovered. The whole counselling process is a rediscovery of yourself. Because of what you have experienced, this discovery will be of a new self. Some childhood memories can be triggered by quite unusual sets of circumstances.

David:

I was in a convalescent home – it was about five months after my assault and I think my depression was at its very worst. I had not tried to end my life, but I had thought about it for several days.

Then I opened a book that I had been lent. Inside I found a piece of poetry which I remembered hearing at some time during my childhood. It was written for Violette Szabo who was in the British resistance working in France during the Second World War. The poem was written by her husband, and Violette used it as her code key whilst working behind enemy lines. I had first heard the poem 26 years earlier when, as a child of nine, I watched the film Carve Her Name with Pride. *I copied the poem onto a scrap of paper.*

> The life that I have is all that I have,
> The life that I have is yours.
> The love that I have of the life that I have,
> Is yours and yours and yours.
> A sleep I shall have, a rest I shall have,
> Yet death will be but a pause.
> For the peace of my years in the long green grass,
> Will be yours and yours and yours.

I kept that piece of paper in my pocket for months. Every time I felt low I would read it. I was amazed that I had remembered its significance in the film I had seen so long ago.

It gave me a strength. A strength to fight my way out of the depression I was in. I decided that many people had suffered far worse than I. I had not been held prisoner, tortured and shot, which was the fate of Violette Szabo.

Had I not rediscovered that childhood memory I don't think the discovery of that poem would have held any significance for me.

Many PTSD sufferers have explained how their experience has reshaped their way of life. It has given them a new set of priorities. There is also a strong view amongst those who have recovered from PTSD that they have a greater understanding of the problems of others. They can identify with the needs of other victims, and on many occasions former sufferers have turned counsellor and helped other victims overcome their fears.

Graham:
I find that my ideals and values of life have completely changed, for the better, may I add. Coming to terms with admitting that I was suffering from PTSD was one of the biggest hurdles, but once I'd accepted it things started to improve.

Many victims also have interesting comments on the subject of counselling, and sticking with it when it gets tough (something PTSD sufferers are not very good at).

Richard:
I suppose our minds automatically shut off when we are told something very unpleasant, and it is only when we are forced to face it that we have an understanding of what has happened.

Even those sufferers who feel they have made a good

recovery from PTSD show an element of caution in their comments.

Cindy:
I still feel a bit wobbly on occasions. I'm sure this will go in time, and I really can't see me being as bad as I was — although, as they say, you have to be prepared for the odd setback. I have felt a bit dizzy on occasions (thought it might be the start of a panic attack) but it hasn't developed into anything major and it definitely hasn't stopped me doing anything.

Looking at the positive side of Post-Traumatic Stress Disorder, the long recovery period gives ample time for reflection and consideration of the future. This can, for a few, be a bleak prospect, but with encouragement and guidance the future can take on a very positive air.

As a victim, you must be able to make sense of what has happened to you in such a way that it allows you to continue with the rest of your life. You have been unfairly treated by life's fortunes. Consequently, you must devise a plan which hastens recovery, restores self-esteem and provides a positive reason for existence. Start to regard the bottle of life as being half-full, not half-empty.

Playing snakes and ladders is different for every player. Some make steady progress up the game board while others rush ahead, only to land on a snake and be brought back down the board. As the game nears its conclusion, players tokens will gather near the top of the board while they wait for the shake of the dice that will give them the exact number required to finish the game. One or two lucky players may shake that number at the first roll of the dice. Some may spend long periods of time waiting for the right number to fall, slowly edging nearer and nearer to the 100 square. Eventually, every player will finish the game, but some will have taken much longer than others. Those of you who have played snakes and ladders will know that at the start it is quite impossible to predict who will win, or how long the game will take to play. Nobody can provide that information.

What is for sure, though, is that the longer you delay the start of the game, the later in the day you will finish it. People with Post-Traumatic Stress Disorder get better because they're tackling their problem and living with it. They are not avoiding it.

From our early years we are told the old adage that every cloud has a silver lining. Well, every silver lining has a price. You have already paid the price, and your task now is to seek out the silver lining. Remind yourself that it *is* possible to put your experience behind you. Today is the first day of the rest of your life.

Believe me, there will come a time when you regain control of your past, and your past will no longer control you.

References

CHAPTER 1

1 Austin, T. 1967. *Aberfan: the story of a disaster.* London: Hutchinson.
2 Erikson, K. 1976. *Everything in Its Path: Destruction of Community in the Buffalo Creek Flood.* New York: Simon & Schuster.
3 Helzer, J. *et al.* 1987. 'Post-Traumatic Stress Disorder in the General Population: Findings of the Epidemiologic Catchment Area Survey, *New England Journal of Medicine* 317: 1630-4.
4 Ravenscroft, T. 1993. Report of a thesis into Post-Traumatic Stress Disorder in the London Ambulance Service.
5 Turnbull, Dr G. 1993. (Quote) Wroughton RAF Hospital, Wiltshire, England.
6 Waite, T. 1993. *Taken on Trust.* London: Hodder & Stoughton.
7 Smith, G. 1986. 'The power of intrusion: Child sexual abuse', *Adoption and Fostering* 10: 13-18.
8 Parkinson, F. 1993. *Post-Trauma Stress.* London: Sheldon Press.

CHAPTER 3

1 DSM III R. 1987. *American Psychiatric Association Diagnostic and Statistical Manual of Mental Disorders* (3rd edition, revised).
2 Scott, M. & Stradling, S. 1992. *Counselling for Post-Traumatic Stress Disorder.* London: Sage.
3 Herman, J. 1992. *Trauma and Recovery.* Pandora.
4 Flannery, R. 1992. *Post-Traumatic Stress Disorder: The Victim's Guide to Healing and Recovery.* New York: Crossroad.
5 Snaith, R. *et al.* 1978. 'A clinical scale for the self-assessment of irritability', *British Journal of Psychiatry* 132: 164-71.
6 Parkinson, F. 1993. *Post-Trauma Stress.* London: Sheldon Press.

CHAPTER 5

1 Flannery, R. 1992. *Post-traumatic Stress Disorder: The Victim's Guide to Healing and Recovery.* New York: Crossroad.
2 Kinchin, D. 1992. 'Telephobia', *The Nursing Times* 88: 52.
3 Cohen, D. 1991. *Aftershock.* London: Paladin.
4 Stern, G. 1976. *The Buffalo Creek Disaster.* New York: Vintage Books.
5 Herman, J. 1992. *Trauma and Recovery.* Pandora.
6 Smith, G. 1989. 'The traumatic response cycle: working with adult survivors of childhood sexual abuse', *Clinical Psychology Forum* 22: 38-43.
7 Parkinson, F. 1993. *Post-Trauma Stress.* London: Sheldon Press.

8 Ravenscroft, T. 1993. Report of a thesis into Post-Traumatic Stress Disorder in the London Ambulance Service.

CHAPTER 6

1 Turnbull, Dr G. 1993. (Quote) Wroughton RAF Hospital, Wiltshire, England.
2 Muss, D. 1991. *The Trauma Trap.* London: Doubleday.
3 Ibid.

CHAPTER 7

1 Hammersley, D. & Beeley, L. 1992. 'The Effects of Medication on Counselling', *Counselling 3:* 162–4.
2 Kluft, R. 1989. Course on Treatment of Multiple Personality Disorder, Annual Meeting of the American Psychiatric Association.
   Herman, J. 1992. *Trauma and Recovery.* Pandora.
3 Scott, M. & Stradling, S. 1992. *Counselling for Post-traumatic Stress Disorder.* London: Sage.
4 Richards, D. & Rose, J. 1991. 'Exposure Therapy for P.T.S.D.', *British Journal of Psychiatry* 158: 836–40.
5 Kinchin, D. 1993. 'Heads in the Sand', *Police Review* (February).
6 DeDomenico, G. 1982. 'Pain relief with Interferential Therapy', *Australian Journal of Physiotherapy* 28: 14–18.
7 Wildwood, C. 1992. *Holistic Aromatherapy.* London: Thorsons.

CHAPTER 8

1 Miller, J. 1974. *Aberfan: A disaster and its aftermath.* London: Constable.
2 Terr, L. 1981. 'Psychic Trauma in Children: Observations following the Chowchilla school-bus kidnapping', *American Journal of Psychiatry* 138: 1.
3 Terr, L. 1983. 'Chowchilla revisited: The effects of Psychic Trauma four years after a school-bus kidnapping', *American Journal of Psychiatry* 140: 12.
4 Kinchin, D. 1988. 'Fatal Accident: Child involved', *Police Review* 1380-1.
5 Brett, Spitzen & Williams, 1988. 'DSM-III-R criteria for post-traumatic stress disorder', *American Journal of Psychiatry* 145 (10) 1232-6.
6 Scott, M. & Stradling, S. 1992. *Counselling for Post-Traumatic Stress Disorder.* London: Sage.
7 Ravenscroft, T. 1993. Report of a thesis into Post-Traumatic Stress Disorder in the London Ambulance Service.

Index